III

CAROLINA INSPIRATIONS
VOLUME III

ALLISON RAMSEY
Architects Inc.   creating sustainable timeless design

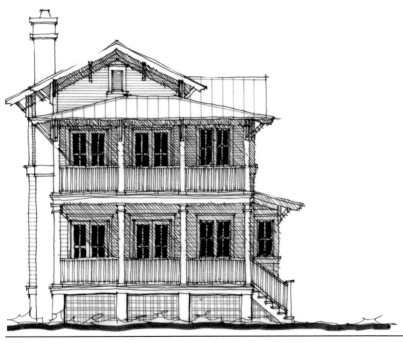

Contents

Carolina Inspirations III

The coastal areas of the South Carolina Lowcountry provide spectacular views of fields, marshes, rivers and the ocean. Most of the houses in this book were designed to complement their natural surroundings while taking full advantage of every possible view and vista. We plan around an old moss-laced live oak tree because it adds to the beauty and grace of your home. We make the windows larger facing the marsh, knowing that when the occasional shrimp boat passes in the distance you'll want to enjoy the moment as long as possible.

Principles of Traditional Architecture

The style and character of Lowcountry traditions and principles of classical architecture have influenced the designs of most of these homes. Any house in this collection, however, can be easily modified for any climate or locale - anywhere in the country. Although the exteriors clearly speak of the past, we have designed these floor plans for the way families live today. Our houses encourage residents to embrace the neighborhood outside their front door. Houses are usually slightly elevated and drawn up close to the sidewalk, so you can talk to your neighbors as they pass by.

Graceful and Inviting Lowcountry Living

Our designs typically feature deep porches, pitched roofs, wide overhangs, dormers, shading, and shadows—the traditional ways people have responded to the Southern climate for generations. Porches and terraces connect the indoors with the outdoors, and tall windows let in lots of light and the gentle flow of those wonderful Carolina seaside summertime breezes. In spirit and stance, our designs evoke beloved images of home. It's all a part of the graceful Southern style of living that the Lowcountry is all about.

What We Believe

Good architecture has a timeless quality that transcends style and period. We are in business to help our clients find the architectural solution that best suits their needs. Simple is what we believe... in efficient designs and an efficient design process. ... in proper proportions. ... in making the spaces fit the family, rather than making the family fit the spaces.... ... in connecting indoors to the outdoors. It's the best way to get more livability for the dollar. We believe in kids and dogs. ... that successful architecture should be accessible to people of all income, education, and background.... and that great architecture is often very simple architecture. We believe that the architect can never be more than half of the successful home design collaboration. We know what we're doing, but only you know how you live. Finally, we believe there is little that is more rewarding than a proud and pleased family delighting in their successfully designed home... A home that we were able to help them put together. That's what we believe.

Why Create A Plan Book Like This?

Designing houses is what we do. We were trained to design houses. We do it every day, and we're good at it. It can be challenging, but it's always fun. We also know how to listen. We understand that designing and building a new home takes a lot of time, effort, emotion and money. The process energizes some potential homeowners; others are paralyzed by the process. Either way, only a few individuals are really sure where to begin or what to do.

The First Step to Your New Home

Designing and building a house is not something you do every day. For most people, it's something you will do once or twice in a lifetime. We want to make it as easy and enjoyable as possible. With this is mind, we came up with the idea of an architectural reference book. In this book are 100 or so floor plans and elevations that represent a variety of the hundreds of traditional homes we've designed. They are presented here to give you ideas of what might work best for you. This plan book is a starting point for you to begin putting together the types of spaces and rooms that best suit your needs and desires. Think of it as a collection of references to help you get started on your perfect house. So, get out your pencil and have at it. Be creative and have some fun. And remember it's going to be your home. We said earlier that we want to be able to bring successful architecture to more people. It is through this book that we intend to begin the process. If the house you've been hoping for is in this book, we'll get you the plans. If the perfect house for you is one of ours with some changes here and there, we'll be happy to get them done. If after looking at all these plans, you'd like us to design a custom house for you from the ground up—-we'd love to help. Or, if all you want to do is call, say hello and ask a question or two, that will be fine too. We're here. We love architecture and we love talking to people who believe what we believe about architecture. We hope you enjoy the book and look forward to hearing from you

How to read:
Carolina Inspirations III

We have learned, and are always learning, what is useful to you; the plan buyer, developer, builder, or homeowner. In Carolina Inspirations II we added overall width and length dimensions to our plan pages. For Carolina Inspirations III we have added "Height to Ridge" and "Individual web addresses" for each plan. Thats right, soon you will easily find the Allison Ramsey home plan online simply by typing in a web address, then buy the plan or download a pdf . Wow! That is convenient, simple, and useful.

As mentioned above our standard information block has retained the info you have come to expect in our planbooks plus new details.

- Each plan has a name and an identification number.

- Under the Plan name id the web address for that particular plan page pdf.

- The Floor plans have the individual square footages and a total heated and cooled square footage is given in the information box.

- Height to Ridge (as described below)

- Number of Bedrooms and Bathrooms contained in the plan.

We hope that you will enjoy this planbook, call us with any questions, and of course find the plan that suites your needs and has the look you love!

THE DUKE STREET

WWW.ALLISONRAMSEYARCHITECT.COM/ PLANS/III/THECRAVEN/PDF

Identification #
C0001
Heated square feet
2447

Overall Dimensions
45'-6" x 45'-6"

Height to Ridge
35'-0"

4 Bed/ 3 1/2 Bath

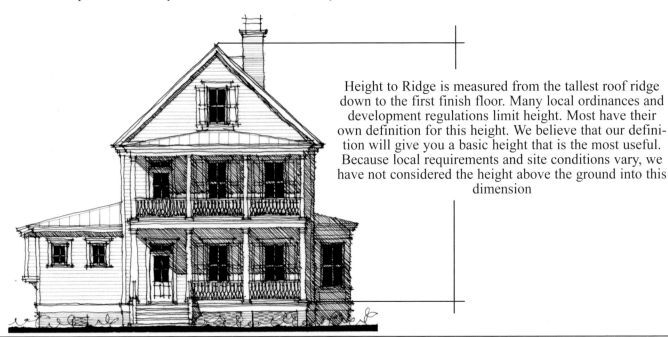

Height to Ridge is measured from the tallest roof ridge down to the first finish floor. Many local ordinances and development regulations limit height. Most have their own definition for this height. We believe that our definition will give you a basic height that is the most useful. Because local requirements and site conditions vary, we have not considered the height above the ground into this dimension

Plans and Designs

This collection of plans, as well as this planbook, have been checked for accuracy, coordination, and overall quality. There may be small differences from the schematic plans shown here and the actual construction documents. Please feel free to contact us with any uncertainties or questions you may have.

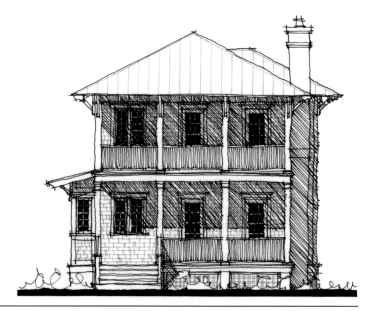

ARA
ALLISON RAMSEY
Architects Inc. creating sustainable timeless design

THE CRAVEN
WWW.ALLISONRAMSEYARCHITECTS.COM/
THECRAVEN.PDF

Identification #
C0508
Heated square feet
2182

Overall Dimensions
31'-4" x 71'-4"

Height to Ridge
30'-1"

4 Bed/ 3 1/2 Bath

First Floor Plan
1354 square feet

Second Floor Plan
828 square feet

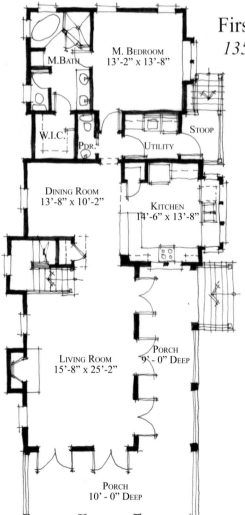

M.Bath

M. Bedroom
13'-2" x 13'-8"

W.I.C.

Stoop

Pdr.

Utility

Dining Room
13'-8" x 10'-2"

Kitchen
14'-6" x 13'-8"

Living Room
15'-8" x 25'-2"

Porch
9'-0" Deep

Porch
10'-0" Deep

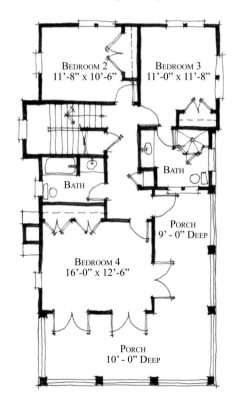

Bedroom 2
11'-8" x 10'-6"

Bedroom 3
11'-0" x 11'-8"

Bath

Bath

Bedroom 4
16'-0" x 12'-6"

Porch
9'-0" Deep

Porch
10'-0" Deep

ALLISON RAMSEY

Architects Inc. creating sustainable timeless design

THE CRAVEN is our newest

interpretation of the classic Charleston sideyard home. Reinvented for todays lifestyles, a convienient master suite located on the first floor, a casual dining room just off the kitchen, and a wide open living room surrounded by generous double story porches fulfill todays needs in a compact vertical footprint. These elements matched with three more large bedrooms upstairs fit the bill for kids, grandkids, parents, or guests.

THE CRAVEN IS AN AMERICAN INSTITUTE OF ARCHITECTS AWARD WINNER

9

ALLISON RAMSEY
Architects Inc. creating sustainable timeless design

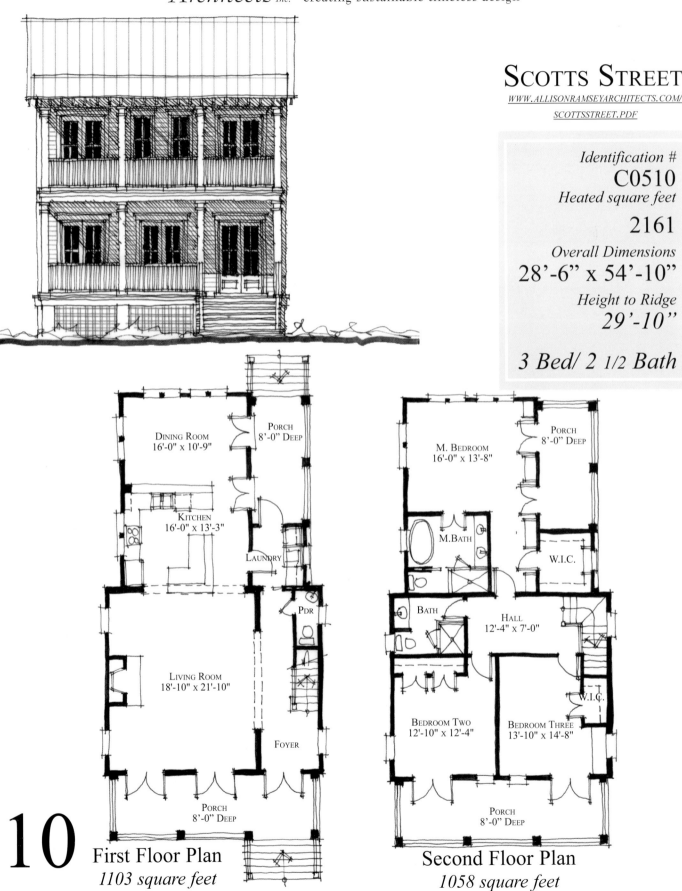

SCOTTS STREET

*WWW.ALLISONRAMSEYARCHITECTS.COM/
SCOTTSSTREET.PDF*

Identification #
C0510
Heated square feet

2161

Overall Dimensions
28'-6" x 54'-10"

Height to Ridge
29'-10"

3 Bed/ 2 1/2 Bath

DINING ROOM
16'-0" x 10'-9"

PORCH
8'-0" DEEP

KITCHEN
16'-0" x 13'-3"

LAUNDRY

PDR

LIVING ROOM
18'-10" x 21'-10"

FOYER

PORCH
8'-0" DEEP

M. BEDROOM
16'-0" x 13'-8"

PORCH
8'-0" DEEP

M.BATH

W.I.C.

BATH

HALL
12'-4" x 7'-0"

W.I.C.

BEDROOM TWO
12'-10" x 12'-4"

BEDROOM THREE
13'-10" x 14'-8"

PORCH
8'-0" DEEP

10

First Floor Plan
1103 square feet

Second Floor Plan
1058 square feet

SPARTINA
COTTAGE

WWW.ALLISONRAMSEYARCHITECTS.COM/
SPARTINACOTTAGE.PDF

Identification #
C0511
Heated square feet
1663
Overall Dimensions
39'-8" x 64'-0"

Height to Ridge
20'-2"

3 Bed/ 2 Bath

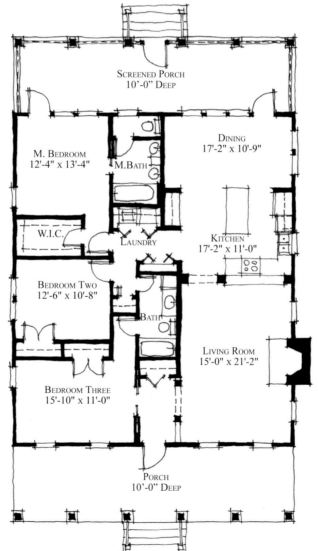

SCREENED PORCH
10'-0" DEEP

M. BEDROOM
12'-4" x 13'-4"

M.BATH

DINING
17'-2" x 10'-9"

W.I.C.

LAUNDRY

KITCHEN
17'-2" x 11'-0"

BEDROOM TWO
12'-6" x 10'-8"

BATH

LIVING ROOM
15'-0" x 21'-2"

BEDROOM THREE
15'-10" x 11'-0"

PORCH
10'-0" DEEP

First Floor Plan
1663 square feet

11

ALLISON RAMSEY

Architects Inc. creating sustainable timeless design

MISES

WWW.ALLISONRAMSEYARCHITECTS.COM/
MISES.PDF

Identification #
C0512
Heated square feet

3044
Overall Dimensions
43'-6" x 78'-4"

Height to Ridge
26'-8"

4 Bed/ 3 Bath

First Floor Plan
2373 square feet

Second Floor Plan
671 square feet

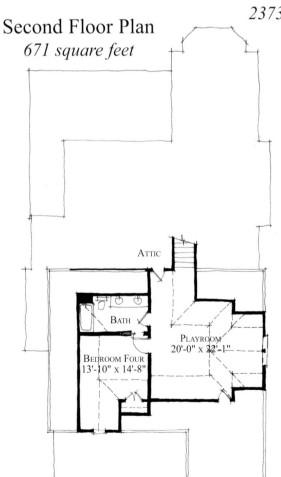

ATTIC

BATH

BEDROOM FOUR
13'-10" x 14'-8"

PLAYROOM
20'-0" x 32'-1"

SCREENED PORCH
12'-0" DEEP

M. BEDROOM
14'-8" x 19'-0"

LIVING ROOM
18'-10" x 20'-0"

M. BATH

LAUNDRY

W.I.C.

KITCHEN
9'-0" x 16'-10"

BEDROOM THREE
OR STUDY
13'-6" x 13'-4"

BREAKFAST
12'-5" x 14'-0"

DINING
15'-0" x 12'-0"

FOYER

BATH

PORCH
8'-0" DEEP

BEDROOM TWO
13'-6" x 12'-0"

12

HOLIDAY COTTAGE

WWW.ALLISONRAMSEYARCHITECTS.COM/
HOLIDAYCOTTAGE.PDF

Identification #

C0513

Heated square feet

1543

Overall Dimensions

28'-6" x 36'-0"

Height to Ridge

33'-2"

2 Bed/ 2 1/2 Bath

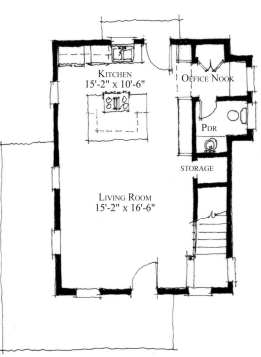

KITCHEN
15'-2" x 10'-6"

OFFICE NOOK

PDR

STORAGE

LIVING ROOM
15'-2" x 16'-6"

First Floor Plan
583 square feet

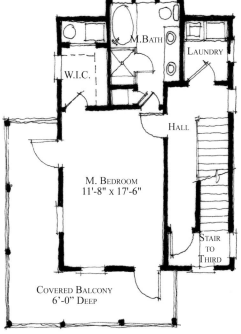

M.BATH

W.I.C.

LAUNDRY

HALL

M. BEDROOM
11'-8" x 17'-6"

STAIR
TO
THIRD

COVERED BALCONY
6'-0" DEEP

Second Floor Plan
577 square feet

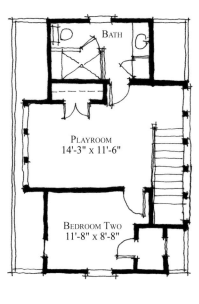

BATH

PLAYROOM
14'-3" x 11'-6"

BEDROOM TWO
11'-8" x 8'-8"

Third Floor Plan
383 square feet

13

RIVER HOUSE

WWW.ALLISONRAMSEYARCHITECTS.COM/RIVERHOUSE.PDF

Identification #

C0514

Heated square feet

1035

Overall Dimensions

29'-6" x 43'-7"

Height to Ridge

24'-4"

1 Bed/ 1 1/2 Bath

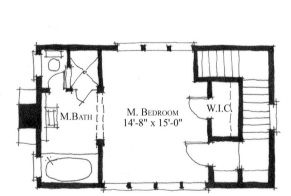

M.BATH

M. BEDROOM
14'-8" x 15'-0"

W.I.C

Second Floor Plan
349 square feet

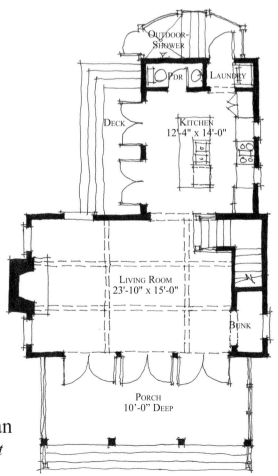

OUTDOOR-
SHOWER

PDR   LAUNDRY

DECK

KITCHEN
12'-4" x 14'-0"

LIVING ROOM
23'-10" x 15'-0"

BUNK

PORCH
10'-0" DEEP

14

First Floor Plan
686 square feet

ALLISON RAMSEY
Architects Inc. creating sustainable timeless design

APPLEGATE PLACE

WWW.ALLISONRAMSEYARCHITECTS.COM/
APPLEGATEPLACE.PDF

Identification #
C0515
Heated square feet

2796

Overall Dimensions
30'-0" x 93'-2"

Height to Ridge
31'-6"

4 Bed/ 3 1/2 Bath

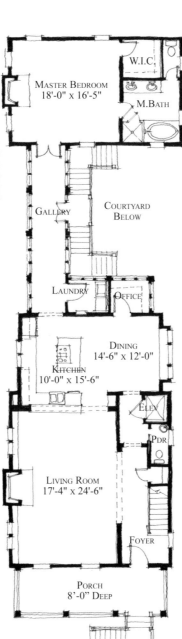

First Floor Plan
1842 square feet

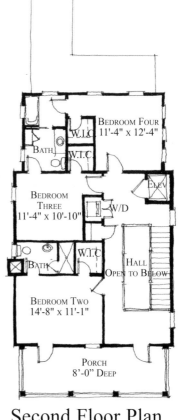

Second Floor Plan
954 square feet

15

ALLISON RAMSEY
Architects Inc. creating sustainable timeless design

HAMMONDS FERRY

WWW.ALLISONRAMSEYARCHITECTS.COM/
HAMMONDSFERRY.PDF

Identification #
C0516
Heated square feet

2104

Overall Dimensions
31'-3" x 73'-0"

Height to Ridge
31'-2"

3 Bed/ 2 1/2 Bath

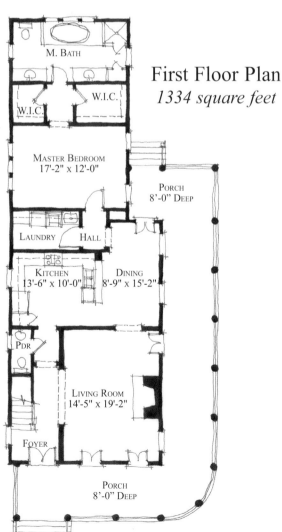

First Floor Plan
1334 square feet

M. BATH

W.I.C.   W.I.C.

MASTER BEDROOM
17'-2" x 12'-0"

PORCH
8'-0" DEEP

LAUNDRY   HALL

KITCHEN
13'-6" x 10'-0"

DINING
8'-9" x 15'-2"

PDR

LIVING ROOM
14'-5" x 19'-2"

FOYER

PORCH
8'-0" DEEP

Second Floor Plan
770 square feet

LOFT/ SITTING
9'-4" x 15'-10"

BEDROOM THREE
10'-3" x 13'-8"

SHARED BATH

BEDROOM TWO
16'-7" x 12'-8"

PORCH
8'-0" DEEP

16

ALLISON RAMSEY

Architects Inc.   creating sustainable timeless design

AIKEN HORSE HOUSE

WWW.ALLISONRAMSEYARCHITECTS.COM/
AIKENHORSEHOUSE.PDF

Identification #

C0517

Heated square feet

1150

Overall Dimensions

45'-0" x 56'-0"

Height to Ridge

33'-2"

2 Bed/ 2 Bath

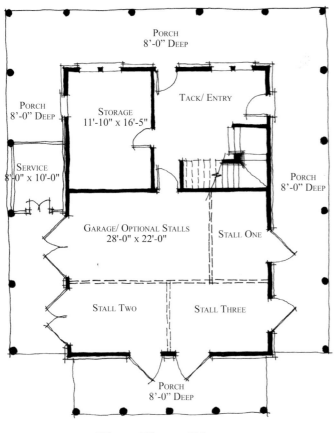

First Floor Plan
1206 square feet

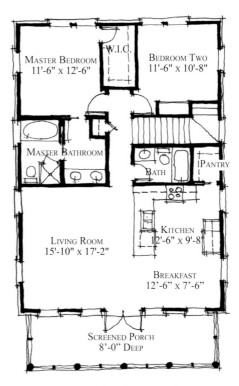

Second Floor Plan
1150 square feet

17

ALLISON RAMSEY

Architects Inc. creating sustainable timeless design

THE HAND KEY

WWW.ALLISONRAMSEYARCHITECTS.COM/
HANDKEY.PDF

Identification #

C0518

Heated square feet

4200

Overall Dimensions
72'-6" x 64'-8"

Height to Ridge
41'-4"

2 Bed/ 2 1/2 Bath

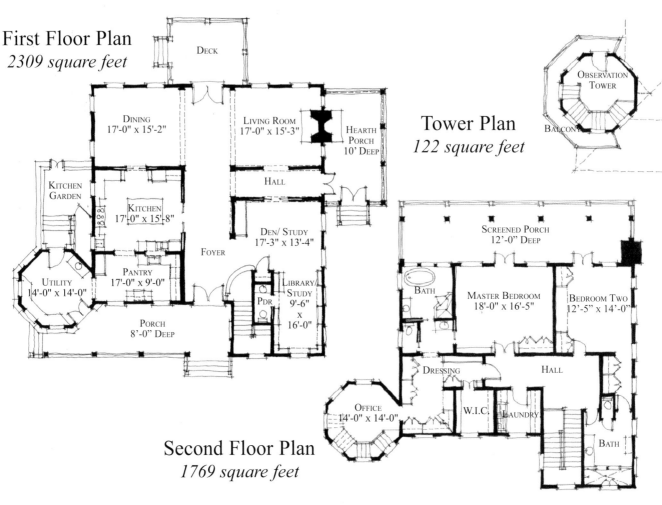

First Floor Plan
2309 square feet

DECK

DINING
17'-0" x 15'-2"

LIVING ROOM
17'-0" x 15'-3"

HEARTH
PORCH
10' Deep

HALL

KITCHEN
GARDEN

KITCHEN
17'-0" x 15'-8"

DEN/ STUDY
17'-3" x 13'-4"

FOYER

UTILITY
14'-0" x 14'-0"

PANTRY
17'-0" x 9'-0"

PDR

LIBRARY/
STUDY
9'-6"
x
16'-0"

PORCH
8'-0" Deep

Tower Plan
122 square feet

OBSERVATION
TOWER

BALCONY

SCREENED PORCH
12'-0" Deep

BATH

MASTER BEDROOM
18'-0" x 16'-5"

BEDROOM TWO
12'-5" x 14'-0"

DRESSING

HALL

OFFICE
14'-0" x 14'-0"

W.I.C.

LAUNDRY

BATH

Second Floor Plan
1769 square feet

THE HAND KEY boasts

lofty 12 foot ceilings, generously proportioned rooms, and is designed for sites with a view. The three story tower provides 360 degree viewing. The adjacent two bedroom guest suite, a separate garage/ office, and two bedrooms are all that are needed in this beautiful Key West flavored home. The large pantry/ working kitchen make this house ideal for large gatherings. The second floor is designed to take advantage of views from the generously sized bedrooms. For cooler nights, the screened porch with masonry fireplace is the place to be.

19

ALLISON RAMSEY

Architects Inc. creating sustainable timeless design

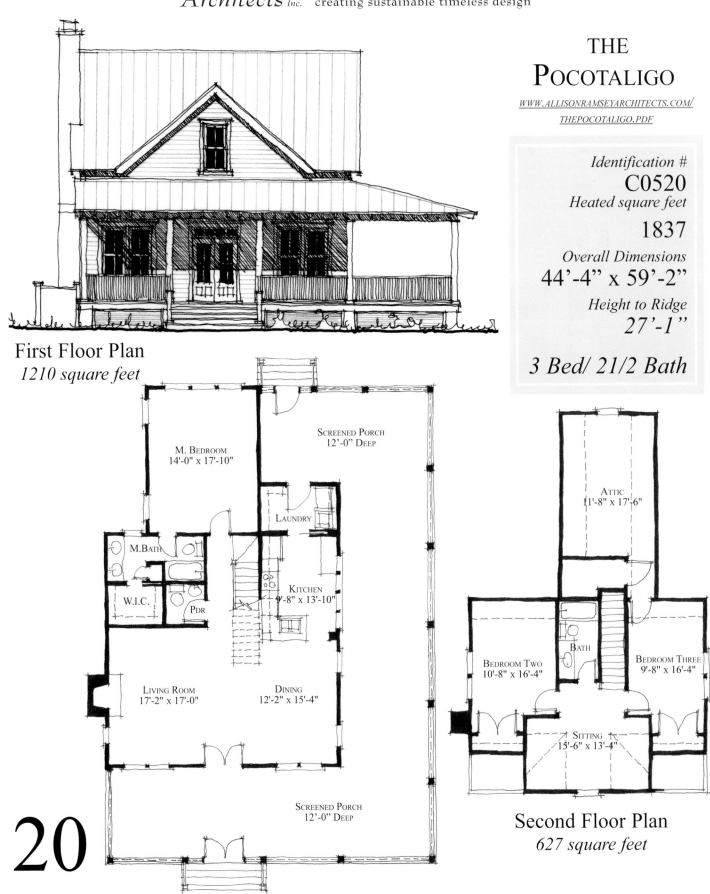

THE
POCOTALIGO

WWW.ALLISONRAMSEYARCHITECTS.COM/
THEPOCOTALIGO.PDF

Identification #
C0520
Heated square feet

1837

Overall Dimensions
44'-4" x 59'-2"

Height to Ridge
27'-1"

3 Bed/ 21/2 Bath

First Floor Plan
1210 square feet

M. BEDROOM
14'-0" x 17'-10"

SCREENED PORCH
12'-0" DEEP

M.BATH

LAUNDRY

W.I.C.

PDR

KITCHEN
9'-8" x 13'-10"

LIVING ROOM
17'-2" x 17'-0"

DINING
12'-2" x 15'-4"

SCREENED PORCH
12'-0" DEEP

ATTIC
11'-8" x 17'-6"

BEDROOM TWO
10'-8" x 16'-4"

BATH

BEDROOM THREE
9'-8" x 16'-4"

SITTING
15'-6" x 13'-4"

Second Floor Plan
627 square feet

20

ARA
ALLISON RAMSEY
Architects Inc. creating sustainable timeless design

CAMDEN DUPLEX

WWW.ALLISONRAMSEYARCHITECTS.COM/
CAMDENDUPLEX.PDF

Identification #
C0521
Heated square feet
1985 *(992 each)*
Overall Dimensions
33'-4" x 47'-10"
Height to Ridge
27'-4"

2 Bed/ 2 Bath

First Floor Plan
1180 square feet total

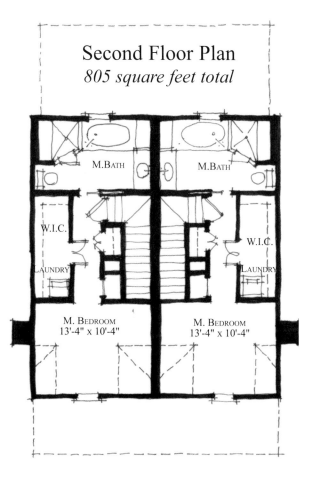

Second Floor Plan
805 square feet total

M.BATH   M.BATH

W.I.C.   W.I.C.

LAUNDRY   LAUNDRY

M. BEDROOM
13'-4" x 10'-4"

M. BEDROOM
13'-4" x 10'-4"

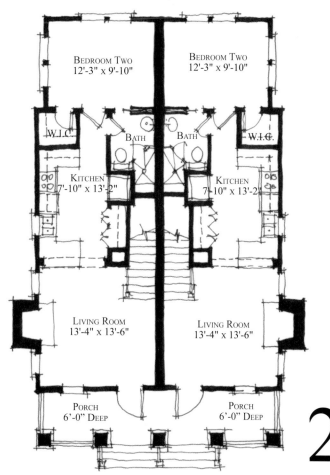

BEDROOM TWO
12'-3" x 9'-10"

BEDROOM TWO
12'-3" x 9'-10"

W.I.C.   BATH   BATH   W.I.C.

KITCHEN
7'-10" x 13'-2"

KITCHEN
7'-10" x 13'-2"

LIVING ROOM
13'-4" x 13'-6"

LIVING ROOM
13'-4" x 13'-6"

PORCH
6'-0" DEEP

PORCH
6'-0" DEEP

21

ALLISON RAMSEY

Architects Inc.   creating sustainable timeless design

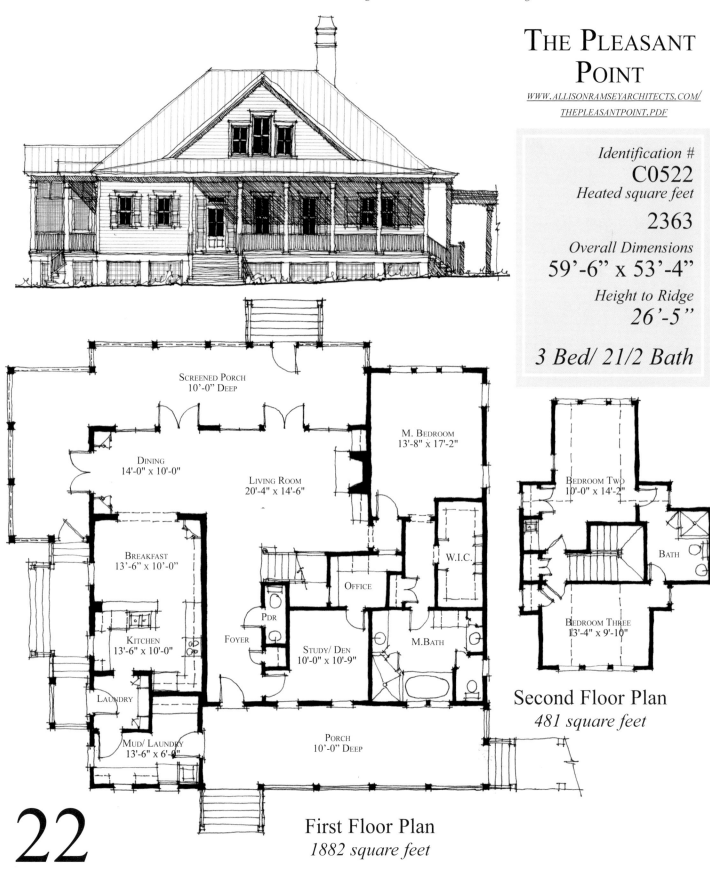

THE PLEASANT POINT

WWW.ALLISONRAMSEYARCHITECTS.COM/
THEPLEASANTPOINT.PDF

Identification #
C0522
Heated square feet

2363

Overall Dimensions
59'-6" x 53'-4"

Height to Ridge
26'-5"

3 Bed/ 2 1/2 Bath

SCREENED PORCH
10'-0" DEEP

M. BEDROOM
13'-8" x 17'-2"

DINING
14'-0" x 10'-0"

LIVING ROOM
20'-4" x 14'-6"

BEDROOM TWO
10'-0" x 14'-2"

BREAKFAST
13'-6" x 10'-0"

W.I.C.

BATH

OFFICE

KITCHEN
13'-6" x 10'-0"

PDR

FOYER

M.BATH

BEDROOM THREE
13'-4" x 9'-10"

STUDY/ DEN
10'-0" x 10'-9"

LAUNDRY

MUD/ LAUNDRY
13'-6" x 6'-0"

PORCH
10'-0" DEEP

Second Floor Plan
481 square feet

22

First Floor Plan
1882 square feet

THE LUCY CREEK

WWW.ALLISONRAMSEYARCHITECTS.COM/
THELUCYCREEK.PDF

Identification #
C0523
Heated square feet

2944

Overall Dimensions
38'-4" x 58'-4"

Height to Ridge
30'-6"

4 Bed/ 3 Bath

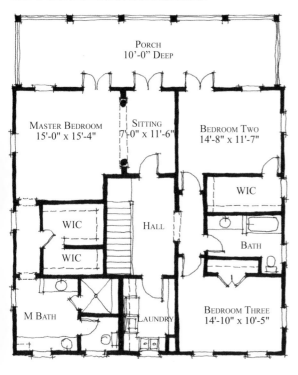

PORCH
10'-0" DEEP

MASTER BEDROOM
15'-0" x 15'-4"

SITTING
7'-0" x 11'-6"

BEDROOM TWO
14'-8" x 11'-7"

WIC

WIC

WIC

HALL

BATH

M BATH

LAUNDRY

BEDROOM THREE
14'-10" x 10'-5"

Second Floor Plan
1367 square feet

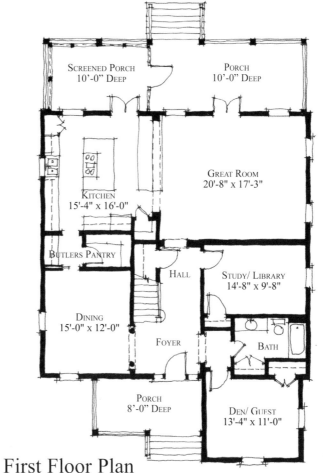

SCREENED PORCH
10'-0" DEEP

PORCH
10'-0" DEEP

KITCHEN
15'-4" x 16'-0"

GREAT ROOM
20'-8" x 17'-3"

BUTLERS PANTRY

HALL

STUDY/ LIBRARY
14'-8" x 9'-8"

DINING
15'-0" x 12'-0"

FOYER

BATH

PORCH
8'-0" DEEP

DEN/ GUEST
13'-4" x 11'-0"

First Floor Plan
1577 square feet

23

ALLISON RAMSEY

Architects Inc. creating sustainable timeless design

Forest Manse

WWW.ALLISONRAMSEYARCHITECTS.COM/
FORESTMANSE.PDF

Identification #

C0524

Heated square feet

2926

Overall Dimensions

47'-6" x 52'-0"

Height to Ridge

29'-8"

4 Bed/ 4 1/2 Bath

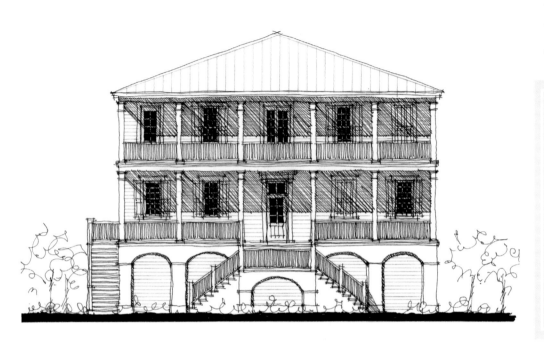

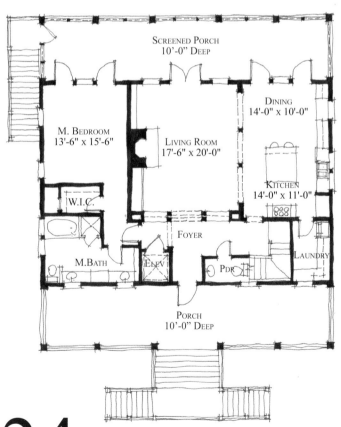

First Floor Plan
1504 square feet

24

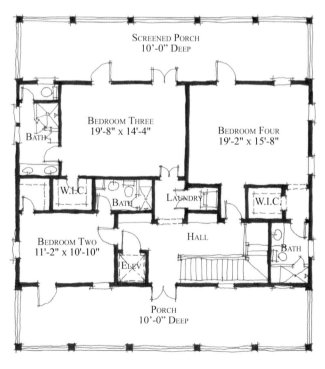

Second Floor Plan
1422 square feet

*Garage Plan Included

ALLISON RAMSEY
Architects Inc. creating sustainable timeless design

Augusta Avenue

WWW.ALLISONRAMSEYARCHITECTS.COM/
AUGUSTAAVENUE.PDF

Identification #
C0525
Heated square feet
1558/1919 *w/ optional*

Overall Dimensions
31'-8" x 60'-4"

Height to Ridge
26'-1"

w/ optional
4 Bed/ 3 1/2 Bath

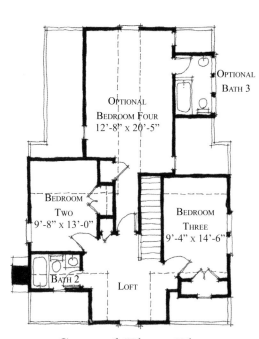

Second Floor Plan
505 square feet
361 optional square feet

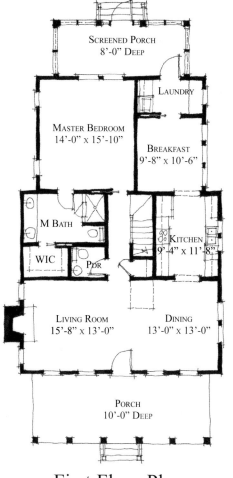

First Floor Plan
1177 square feet

25

ALLISON RAMSEY

Architects Inc. creating sustainable timeless design

RAMSEY

WWW.ALLISONRAMSEYARCHITECTS.COM/
THERAMSEY.PDF

Identification #
C0526
Heated square feet

1970

Overall Dimensions
42'-10" x 59'-0"

Height to Ridge
25'-6"

4 Bed/ 3 Bath

First Floor Plan
1496 square feet

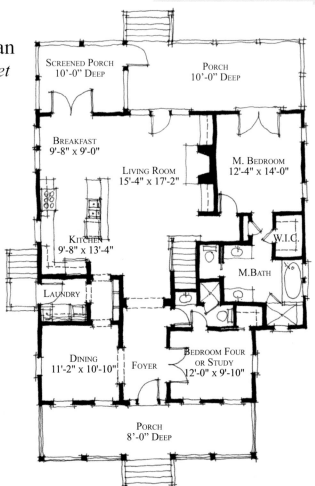

SCREENED PORCH 10'-0" DEEP
PORCH 10'-0" DEEP
BREAKFAST 9'-8" x 9'-0"
LIVING ROOM 15'-4" x 17'-2"
M. BEDROOM 12'-4" x 14'-0"
KITCHEN 9'-8" x 13'-4"
W.I.C.
M.BATH
LAUNDRY
DINING 11'-2" x 10'-10"
FOYER
BEDROOM FOUR OR STUDY 12'-0" x 9'-10"
PORCH 8'-0" DEEP

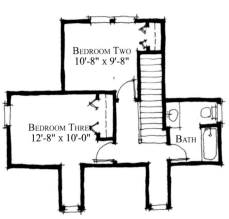

BEDROOM TWO 10'-8" x 9'-8"
BEDROOM THREE 12'-8" x 10'-0"
BATH

Second Floor Plan
474 square feet

26

ALLISON RAMSEY

Architects Inc. creating sustainable timeless design

THE LYFORD

WWW.ALLISONRAMSEYARCHITECTS.COM/
THELYFORD.PDF

Identification #
C0527
Heated square feet

1834

Overall Dimensions
27'-4" x 58'-0"

Height to Ridge
28'-0"

3 Bed/ 2 1/2 Bath

First Floor Plan
1208 square feet

M. BATH

M. BEDROOM
15'-6" x 15'-8"

W.I.C.

W.I.C.

KITCHEN
15'-4" x 12'-10"

LAUNDRY

PDR

DINING
12'-8" x 12'-0"

PORCH
8'-0" DEEP

LIVING ROOM
15'-4" x 15'-10"

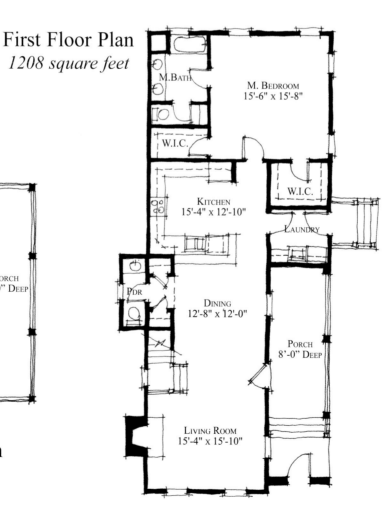

BEDROOM THREE
15'-4" x 11'-10"

HALL

SHARED
BATH

W.I.C.

PORCH
8'-0" DEEP

BEDROOM TWO
15'-4" x 11'-10"

Second Floor Plan
626 square feet

27

ALLISON RAMSEY

Architects Inc.   creating sustainable timeless design

CARSON HOUSE

WWW.ALLISONRAMSEYARCHITECTS.COM/
CARSONHOUSE.PDF

Identification #

C0528

Heated square feet

973

Overall Dimensions
22'-4" x 41'-8"

Height to Ridge
22'-8"

2 Bed/ 2 Bath

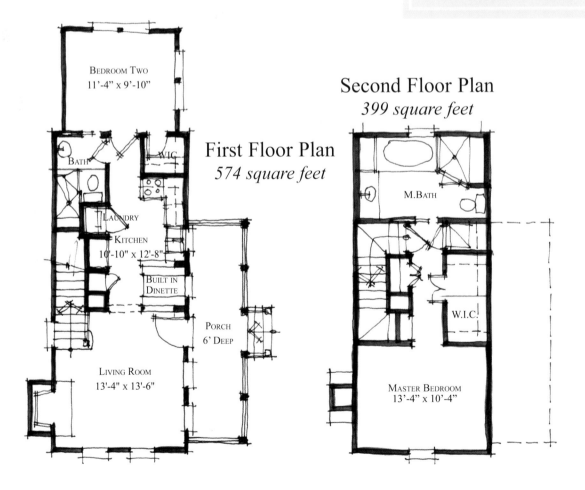

First Floor Plan
574 square feet

BEDROOM TWO
11'-4" x 9'-10"

BATH

WIC

LAUNDRY

KITCHEN
10'-10" x 12'-8"

BUILT IN
DINETTE

PORCH
6' DEEP

LIVING ROOM
13'-4" x 13'-6"

Second Floor Plan
399 square feet

M.BATH

W.I.C.

MASTER BEDROOM
13'-4" x 10'-4"

ALLISON RAMSEY

Architects Inc.   creating sustainable timeless design

CARSON HOUSE is one of our many examples of the "not so big house' concept. A popular concept that speaks of the power of small, well designed spaces that have maximum flexibility and efficiency. This little two bedroom cottage has a cute face, a narrow footprint, and a super cool Master Suite upstairs. Carson House is perfect for a single person, a young couple, or even a family starting out. With its smaller size and sideyard porch Carson House is great for a corner lot, nestled into a row of Charleston sideyard homes, or situated into a small cottage court. Carson house proves "Great things do come in small packages"

CARSON HOUSE IS PART OF AN AMERICAN INSTITUTE OF ARCHITECTS AWARDED PROJECT.

29

ALLISON RAMSEY

Architects Inc. creating sustainable timeless design

THE EAST BEACH

WWW.ALLISONRAMSEYARCHITECTS.COM/
THEEASTBEACH.PDF

Identification #
C0530
Heated square feet

2935

Overall Dimensions
25'-0" x 61'-4"

Height to Ridge
37'-0"

4 Bed/ 4 Bath

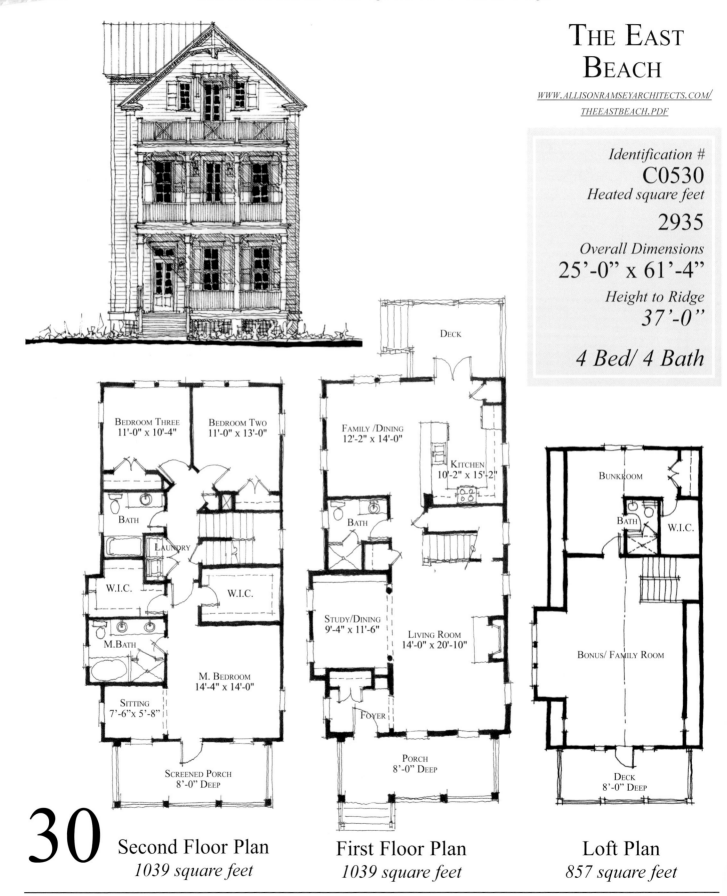

30

Second Floor Plan
1039 square feet

First Floor Plan
1039 square feet

Loft Plan
857 square feet

Architects Inc. creating sustainable timeless design

CHESAPEAKE BUNGALOW

WWW.ALLISONRAMSEYARCHITECTS.COM/
CHESAPEKEBUNGALOW.PDF

Identification #
C0531
Heated square feet

2472

Overall Dimensions
38'-0"x 86'-10"

Height to Ridge
21'-1"

3 Bed/ 2 Bath

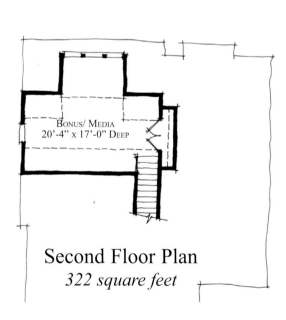

Second Floor Plan
322 square feet

Bonus/ Media
20'-4" x 17'-0" Deep

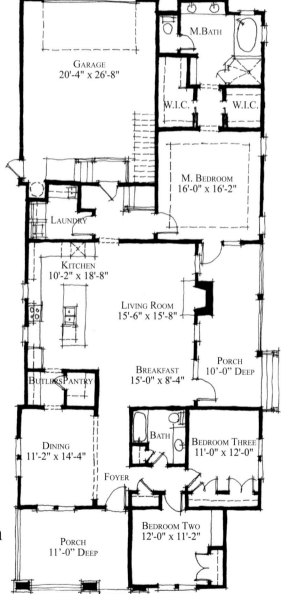

GARAGE
20'-4" x 26'-8"

M.BATH

W.I.C.   W.I.C.

M. BEDROOM
16'-0" x 16'-2"

LAUNDRY

KITCHEN
10'-2" x 18'-8"

LIVING ROOM
15'-6" x 15'-8"

BREAKFAST
15'-0" x 8'-4"

PORCH
10'-0" Deep

BUTLERS PANTRY

BATH

BEDROOM THREE
11'-0" x 12'-0"

DINING
11'-2" x 14'-4"

FOYER

First Floor Plan
2150 square feet

PORCH
11'-0" Deep

BEDROOM TWO
12'-0" x 11'-2"

31

ALLISON RAMSEY ARCHITECTS INC. • PHONE: 843.986.0559 • ONLINE: www.allisonramseyarchitects.com

ALLISON RAMSEY
Architects Inc. creating sustainable timeless design

CHAPIN COTTAGE

WWW.ALLISONRAMSEYARCHITECTS.COM/
CHAPINCOTTAGE.PDF

Identification #

C0532

Heated square feet

2342

Overall Dimensions

42'-7" x 58'-6"

Height to Ridge

26'-2"

3 Bed/ 3 Bath

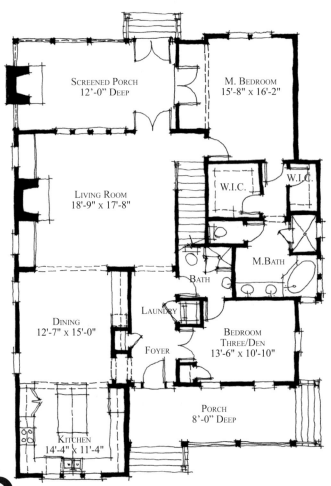

SCREENED PORCH
12'-0" DEEP

M. BEDROOM
15'-8" x 16'-2"

LIVING ROOM
18'-9" x 17'-8"

W.I.C.

W.I.C.

M.BATH

BATH

DINING
12'-7" x 15'-0"

LAUNDRY

FOYER

BEDROOM
THREE/DEN
13'-6" x 10'-10"

PORCH
8'-0" DEEP

KITCHEN
14'-4" x 11'-4"

32

Second Floor Plan
1756 square feet

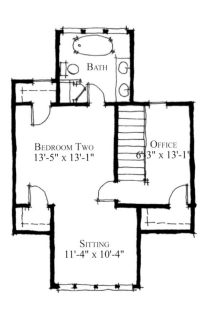

BATH

BEDROOM TWO
13'-5" x 13'-1"

OFFICE
6'-3" x 13'-1"

SITTING
11'-4" x 10'-4"

Second Floor Plan
586 square feet

ALLISON RAMSEY
Architects Inc. creating sustainable timeless design

Low Country Retreat

WWW.ALLISONRAMSEYARCHITECTS.COM/
LOWCOUNTRYRETREAT.PDF

Identification #
C0533
Heated square feet

1266/1441
Overall Dimensions
36'-10" x 37'-8"

Height to Ridge
22'-11"

3 Bed/ 2 1/2 Bath

Optional Second Floor Plans

Second Floor A
426 square feet

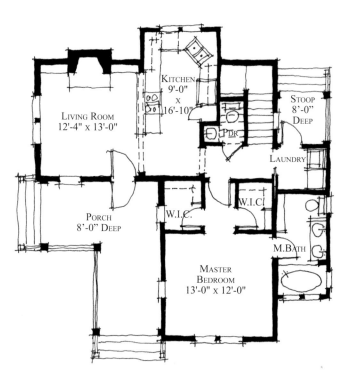

First Floor Plan
840 square feet

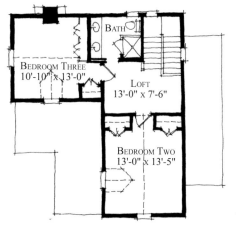

Second Floor B
601 square feet

33

ALLISON RAMSEY

Architects Inc. creating sustainable timeless design

DAD'S GETAWAY

WWW.ALLISONRAMSEYARCHITECTS.COM/
DADSGETAWAY.PDF

Identification #

C0534

Heated square feet

521

Overall Dimensions

38'-0" x 23'-0"

Height to Ridge

17'-2"

1 Bed/ 1 Bath

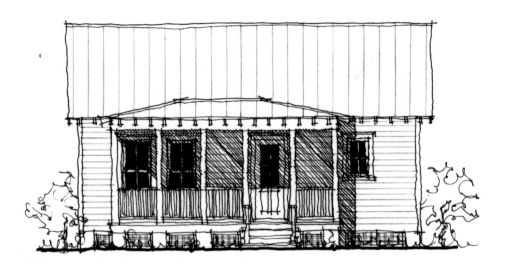

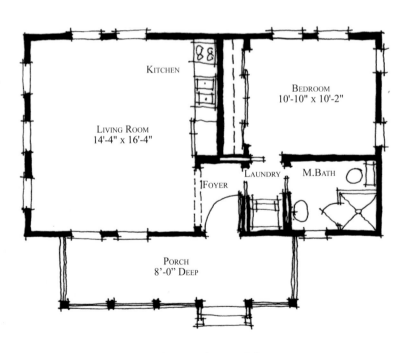

First Floor Plan
521 square feet

34

ALLISON RAMSEY
Architects Inc. creating sustainable timeless design

HAMPTON ROADS

WWW.ALLISONRAMSEYARCHITECTS.COM/
HAMPTONROADS.PDF

Identification #
C0535
Heated square feet
1965
Overall Dimensions
25'-0" x 64'-0"

Height to Ridge
27'-5"

3 Bed/ 2 1/2 Bath

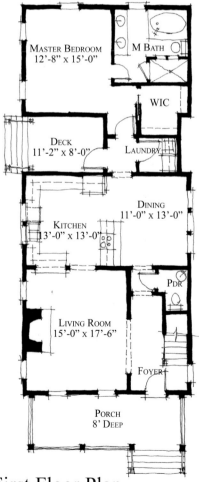

MASTER BEDROOM
12'-8" x 15'-0"

M BATH

WIC

DECK
11'-2" x 8'-0"

LAUNDRY

DINING
11'-0" x 13'-0"

KITCHEN
13'-0" x 13'-0"

PDR

LIVING ROOM
15'-0" x 17'-6"

FOYER

PORCH
8' DEEP

BEDROOM TWO
17'-6" x 13'-2"

WIC

BATH

BEDROOM THREE
16'-0" x 12'-8"

WIC

Second Floor Plan
673 square feet

First Floor Plan
1292 square feet

35

ALLISON RAMSEY

Architects Inc. creating sustainable timeless design

THE DUKE
STREET

WWW.ALLISONRAMSEYARCHITECTS.COM/
THEDUKESTREET.PDF

Identification #
C0536
Heated square feet
1259

Overall Dimensions
32'-6" x 47'-2"

Height to Ridge
15'-9"

4 Bed/ 2 Bath

BEDROOM TWO
10'-4" x 11'-8"

BATH

BEDROOM FOUR
10'-0" x 11'-4"

BATH

BEDROOM THREE
10'-4" x 10'-2"

M. BEDROOM
10'-0" x 12'-4"

LAUNDRY

LIVING ROOM
15'-10" x 13'-2"

DINING
11'-5" x 10'-0"

PORCH
6'-0" DEEP

KITCHEN
11'-7" x 9'-10"

First Floor Plan
1259 square feet

36

ALLISON RAMSEY
Architects Inc. creating sustainable timeless design

CARTER'S MANOR

WWW.ALLISONRAMSEYARCHITECTS.COM/
CARTERSMANOR.PDF

Identification #
C0537
Heated square feet
5066
Overall Dimensions
74'-8" x 58'-0"
Height to Ridge
36'-0"

5 Bed/ 4 1/2 Bath

Third Floor Plan
1059 square feet

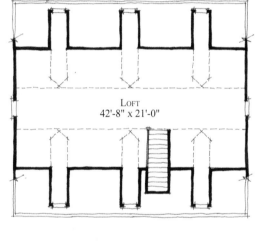

LOFT
42'-8" x 21'-0"

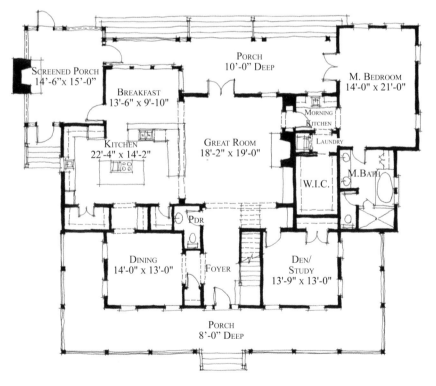

SCREENED PORCH
14'-6"x 15'-0"

BREAKFAST
13'-6" x 9'-10"

PORCH
10'-0" Deep

M. BEDROOM
14'-0" x 21'-0"

MORNING KITCHEN

LAUNDRY

KITCHEN
22'-4" x 14'-2"

GREAT ROOM
18'-2" x 19'-0"

W.I.C.

M.BATH

PDR

DINING
14'-0" x 13'-0"

FOYER

DEN/ STUDY
13'-9" x 13'-0"

PORCH
8'-0" Deep

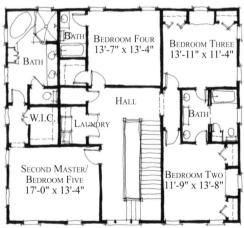

BATH

BATH

BEDROOM FOUR
13'-7" x 13'-4"

BEDROOM THREE
13'-11" x 11'-4"

W.I.C.

LAUNDRY

HALL

BATH

SECOND MASTER/ BEDROOM FIVE
17'-0" x 13'-4"

BEDROOM TWO
11'-9" x 13'-8"

First Floor Plan
2354 square feet

Second Floor Plan
1653 square feet

37

ALLISON RAMSEY
Architects Inc. creating sustainable timeless design

BROAD RIVER COTTAGE

WWW.ALLISONRAMSEYARCHITECTS.COM/
BROADRIVERCOTTAGE.PDF

Identification #
C0028
Heated square feet

1513

Overall Dimensions
26'-0" x 61'-0"

Height to Ridge
26'-0"

3 Bed/ 2 1/2 Bath

Second Floor Plan
456 square feet

DECK
8'-0" DEEP

LAUNDRY

M. BEDROOM
15'-0" x 12'-4"

KITCHEN
10'-0" x 10'-6"

WIC

PDR

M BATH

DINING
10'-0" x 10'-2"

LIVING ROOM
21'-4" x 13'-4"

PORCH
8'-0" DEEP

First Floor Plan
1057 square feet

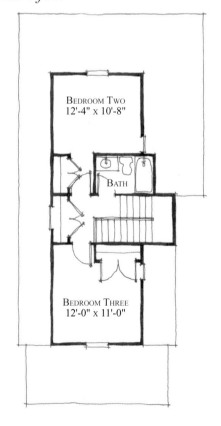

BEDROOM TWO
12'-4" x 10'-8"

BATH

BEDROOM THREE
12'-0" x 11'-0"

THE BROAD RIVER

is an iconic little cottage that has been very popular all over the country. The form is simple which makes the Broad River Cottage appealing to everyone and efficient to build. Ten foot ceilings, eight foot deep porches, open floor plan, and a big rear deck make the cottage extremely livable and marketable. The Broad River Cottage is a great house for more urban neighborhoods as well as rural settings. We have adjusted the details many times to be contextually appropriate. The Broad River Cottage is a narrow plan that lives large and has a great curb appeal.

39

ALLISON RAMSEY

Architects *Inc.*   creating sustainable timeless design

THE NEWPOINT

WWW.ALLISONRAMSEYARCHITECTS.COM/
THENEWPOINT.PDF

Identification #
C0540
Heated square feet

2564

Overall Dimensions
38'-4" x 67'-8"

Height to Ridge
28'-0"

4 Bed/ 3 Bath

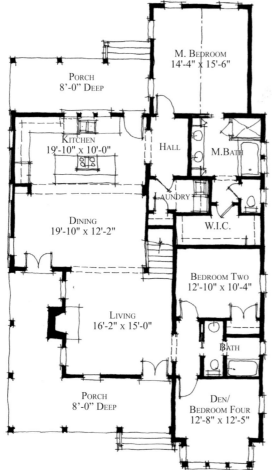

First Floor Plan
1776 square feet

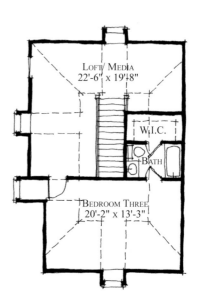

Second Floor Plan
788 square feet

40

ALLISON RAMSEY

Architects Inc. creating sustainable timeless design

THE GOODEAN

WWW.ALLISONRAMSEYARCHITECTS.COM/
GOODEAN.PDF

Identification #

C0541

Heated square feet

2202

Overall Dimensions

38'-6" x 57'-2"

Height to Ridge

29'-2"

4 Bed/ 3 1/2 Bath

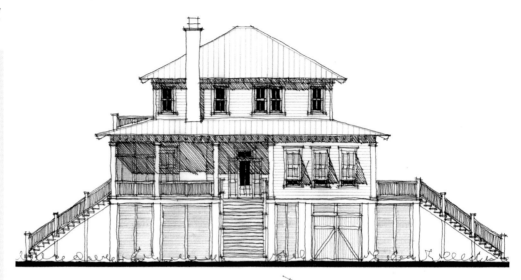

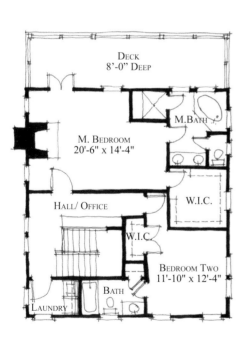

DECK
8'-0" DEEP

M.BATH

M. BEDROOM
20'-6" x 14'-4"

HALL/ OFFICE

W.I.C.

W.I.C.

BEDROOM TWO
11'-10" x 12'-4"

LAUNDRY

BATH

Second Floor Plan
927 square feet

PORCH
8'-0" DEEP

SCREENED PORCH
8'-0" DEEP

KITCHEN/ BREAKFAST
14'-5" x 19'-10"

GREAT ROOM
14'-9" x 14'-5"

FOYER

PDR.

DEN/
BEDROOM FOUR
10'-5" x 10'-0"

BEDROOM THREE
12'-0" x 13'-2"

BATH

PORCH
8'-0" DEEP

DECK
8'-0" DEEP

First Floor Plan
1275 square feet

41

*Garage Plan Included

ALLISON RAMSEY

Architects Inc. creating sustainable timeless design

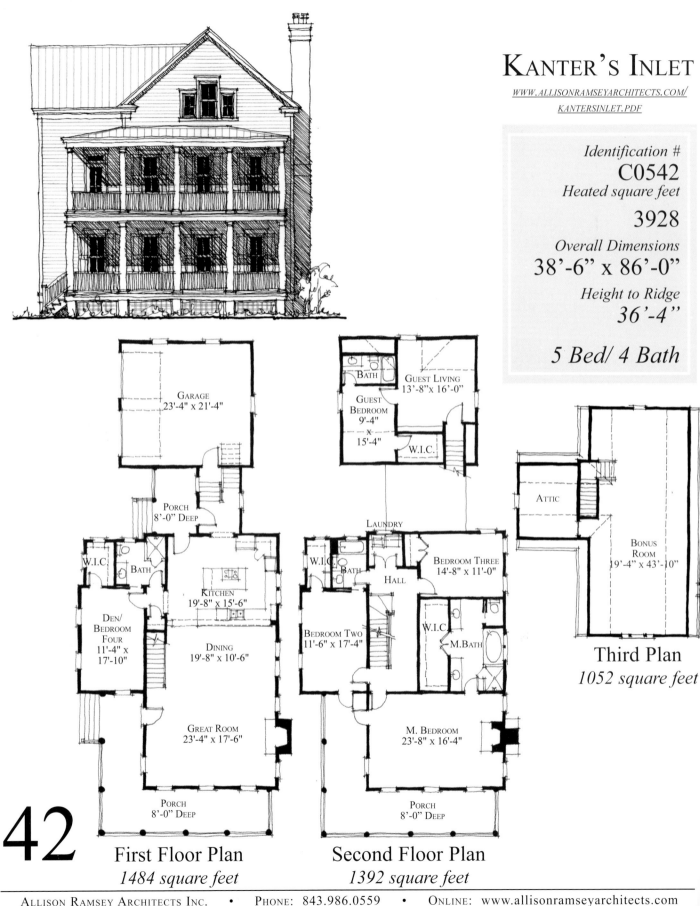

Kanter's Inlet

WWW.ALLISONRAMSEYARCHITECTS.COM/
KANTERSINLET.PDF

Identification #
C0542
Heated square feet
3928
Overall Dimensions
38'-6" x 86'-0"
Height to Ridge
36'-4"

5 Bed/ 4 Bath

GARAGE
23'-4" x 21'-4"

PORCH
8'-0" DEEP

W.I.C.

BATH

DEN/
BEDROOM
FOUR
11'-4" x
17'-10"

KITCHEN
19'-8" x 15'-6"

DINING
19'-8" x 10'-6"

GREAT ROOM
23'-4" x 17'-6"

PORCH
8'-0" DEEP

First Floor Plan
1484 square feet

BATH

GUEST LIVING
13'-8" x 16'-0"

GUEST
BEDROOM
9'-4"
x
15'-4"

W.I.C.

LAUNDRY

W.I.C.

BATH

HALL

BEDROOM THREE
14'-8" x 11'-0"

BEDROOM TWO
11'-6" x 17'-4"

W.I.C.

M.BATH

M. BEDROOM
23'-8" x 16'-4"

PORCH
8'-0" DEEP

Second Floor Plan
1392 square feet

ATTIC

BONUS
ROOM
19'-4" x 43'-10"

Third Plan
1052 square feet

42

ALLISON RAMSEY
Architects Inc. creating sustainable timeless design

DISTANT ISLAND
HOUSE

WWW.ALLISONRAMSEYARCHITECTS.COM/DISTANTISLANDHOUSE.PDF

Identification #
C0543
Heated square feet
2492

Overall Dimensions
70'-8" x 80'-8"

Height to Ridge
19'-11"

3 Bed/ 3 Bath

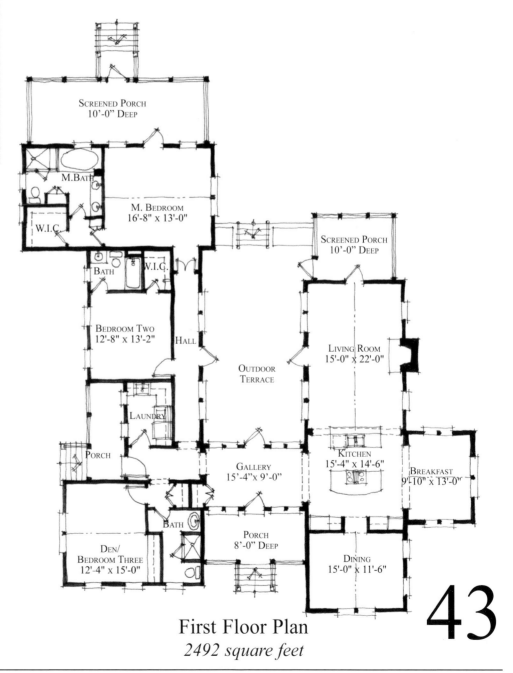

SCREENED PORCH
10'-0" DEEP

M. BATH

M. BEDROOM
16'-8" x 13'-0"

W.I.C.

BATH

W.I.C.

SCREENED PORCH
10'-0" DEEP

BEDROOM TWO
12'-8" x 13'-2"

HALL

OUTDOOR TERRACE

LIVING ROOM
15'-0" x 22'-0"

LAUNDRY

PORCH

GALLERY
15'-4" x 9'-0"

KITCHEN
15'-4" x 14'-6"

BREAKFAST
9'-10" x 13'-0"

BATH

DEN/
BEDROOM THREE
12'-4" x 15'-0"

PORCH
8'-0" DEEP

DINING
15'-0" x 11'-6"

43

First Floor Plan
2492 square feet

ALLISON RAMSEY
Architects Inc. creating sustainable timeless design

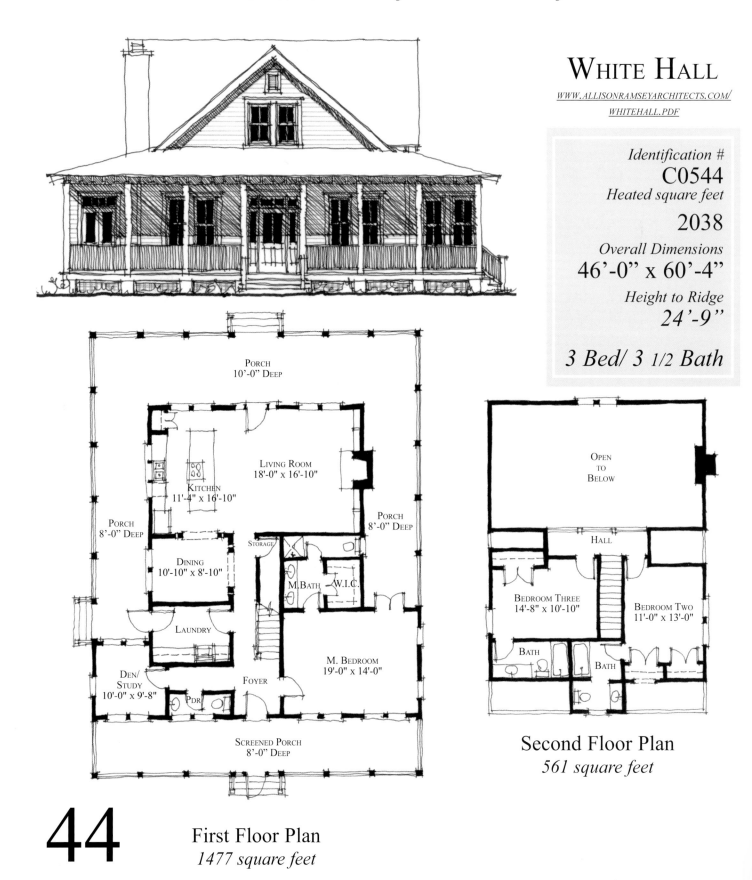

WHITE HALL
WWW.ALLISONRAMSEYARCHITECTS.COM/
WHITEHALL.PDF

Identification #
C0544
Heated square feet

2038

Overall Dimensions
46'-0" x 60'-4"

Height to Ridge
24'-9"

3 Bed/ 3 1/2 Bath

Second Floor Plan
561 square feet

44

First Floor Plan
1477 square feet

ARA
ALLISON RAMSEY
Architects Inc. creating sustainable timeless design

THE SUMMERVILLE

WWW.ALLISONRAMSEYARCHITECTS.COM/
SUMMERVILLE.PDF

Identification #
C0545
Heated square feet

1994

Overall Dimensions
25'-0" x 64'-2"

Height to Ridge
27'-5"

3 Bed/ 2 1/2 Bath

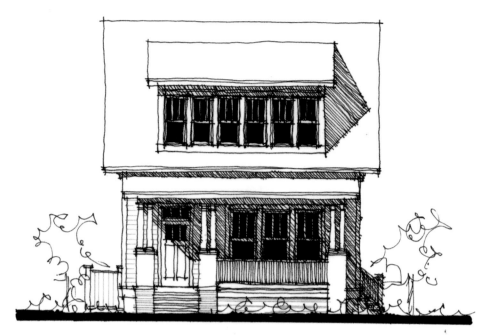

First Floor Plan
1292 square feet

M BATH

MASTER BEDROOM
12'-8" x 15'-4"

DRESSING

WIC

DECK
11'-2" x 8'-0"

DINING
12'-2" x 13'-0"

KITCHEN
12'-2" x 13'-0"

PDR

LIVING ROOM
20'-6" x 17'-9"

FOYER

PORCH
8' DEEP

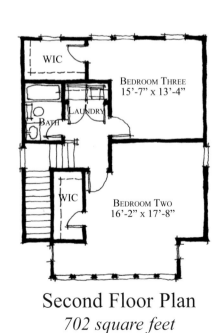

WIC

BEDROOM THREE
15'-7" x 13'-4"

LAUNDRY

BATH

WIC

BEDROOM TWO
16'-2" x 17'-8"

Second Floor Plan
702 square feet

45

ALLISON RAMSEY
Architects Inc. creating sustainable timeless design

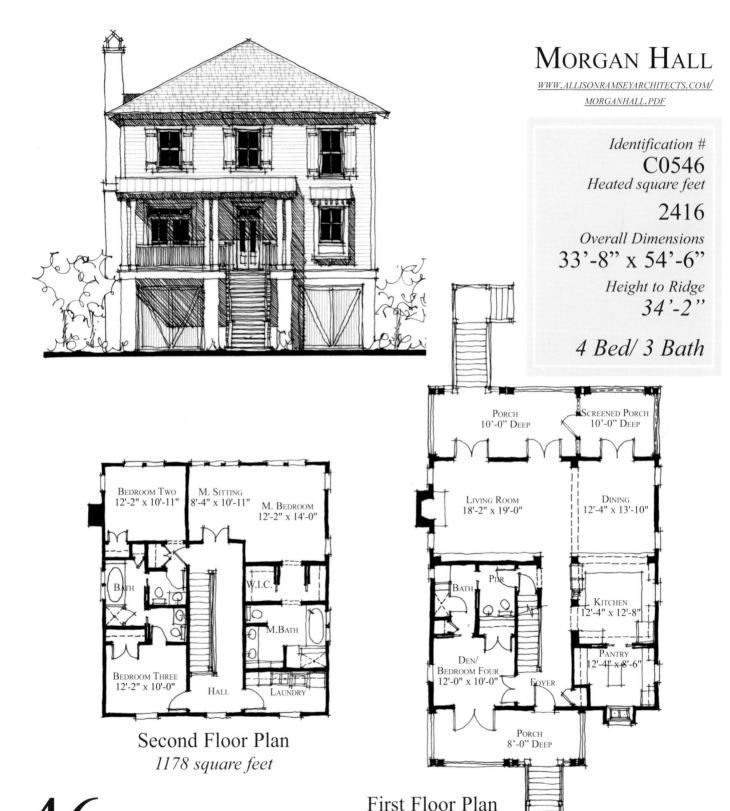

MORGAN HALL

WWW.ALLISONRAMSEYARCHITECTS.COM/
MORGANHALL.PDF

Identification #
C0546
Heated square feet

2416

Overall Dimensions
33'-8" x 54'-6"

Height to Ridge
34'-2"

4 Bed/ 3 Bath

Second Floor Plan
1178 square feet

BEDROOM TWO
12'-2" x 10'-11"

M. SITTING
8'-4" x 10'-11"

M. BEDROOM
12'-2" x 14'-0"

BATH

W.I.C.

M.BATH

BEDROOM THREE
12'-2" x 10'-0"

HALL

LAUNDRY

PORCH
10'-0" DEEP

SCREENED PORCH
10'-0" DEEP

LIVING ROOM
18'-2" x 19'-0"

DINING
12'-4" x 13'-10"

BATH

PDR

KITCHEN
12'-4" x 12'-8"

DEN/
BEDROOM FOUR
12'-0" x 10'-0"

FOYER

PANTRY
12'-4" x 8'-6"

PORCH
8'-0" DEEP

First Floor Plan
1238 square feet

46

*Garage Plan Included

ALLISON RAMSEY
Architects Inc. creating sustainable timeless design

POLLAWANA
ROAD

WWW.ALLISONRAMSEYARCHITECTS.COM/
POLLAWANAROAD.PDF

Identification #
C0547
Heated square feet

2338

Overall Dimensions
56'-8" x 58'-6"

Height to Ridge
27'-9"

3 Bed/ 3 1/2 Bath

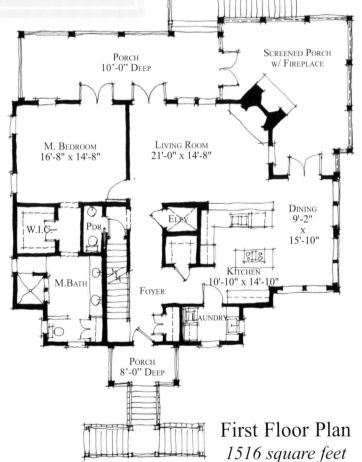

First Floor Plan
1516 square feet

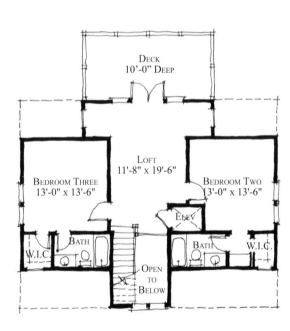

Second Floor Plan
822 square feet

47

Garage Plan Included

ARA
ALLISON RAMSEY
Architects Inc. creating sustainable timeless design

NET WEAVER'S PLACE

WWW.ALLISONRAMSEYARCHITECTS.COM/
NETWEAVERSPLACE.PDF

Identification #
C0548
Heated square feet

3954

Overall Dimensions
87'-6" x 65'-10"

Height to Ridge
30'-11"

4 Bed/ 4 Bath

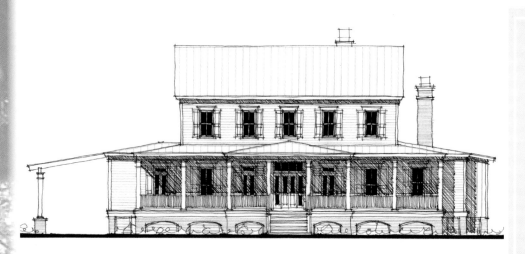

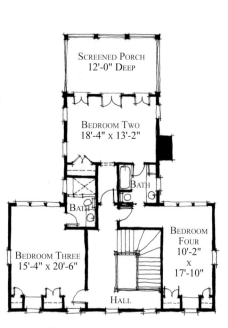

Second Floor Plan
1219 square feet

- Screened Porch 12'-0" Deep
- Bedroom Two 18'-4" x 13'-2"
- Bath
- Bath
- Bedroom Three 15'-4" x 20'-6"
- Bedroom Four 10'-2" x 17'-10"
- Hall

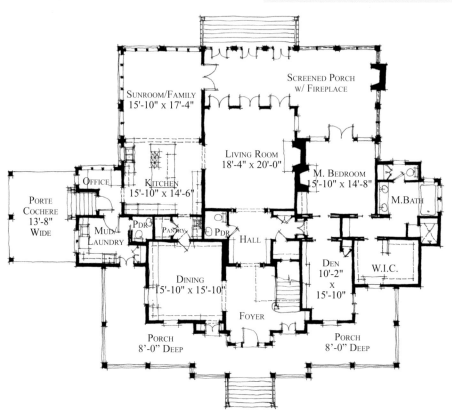

First Floor Plan
2735 square feet

- Sunroom/Family 15'-10" x 17'-4"
- Screened Porch w/ Fireplace
- Living Room 18'-4" x 20'-0"
- M. Bedroom 15'-10" x 14'-8"
- M.Bath
- Office
- Kitchen 15'-10" x 14'-6"
- Porte Cochere 13'-8" Wide
- Mud/ Laundry
- Pdr
- Pantry
- Pdr
- Hall
- Den 10'-2" x 15'-10"
- W.I.C.
- Dining 15'-10" x 15'-10"
- Foyer
- Porch 8'-0" Deep
- Porch 8'-0" Deep

ALLISON RAMSEY

Architects Inc. creating sustainable timeless design

NetWeaver's Place

NetWeaver's Place is modeled after the stately plantation houses found throughout the rural south. Great for large lots and made especially for maximizing that spectacular view at the rear, Net Weavers Place is perfect for that waterfront, marshview, or hilltop site. A great combination of formal and casual spaces truly creates a place where one can unwind, have fun, and enjoy all this house has to offer.

49

ALLISON RAMSEY

Architects Inc. creating sustainable timeless design

DIANE'S FARMHOUSE

WWW.ALLISONRAMSEYARCHITECTS.COM/
DIANESFARMHOUSE.PDF

Identification #
C0550
Heated square feet
3290
Overall Dimensions
70'-0" x 51'-8"
Height to Ridge
32'-6"

5 Bed/ 5 1/2 Bath

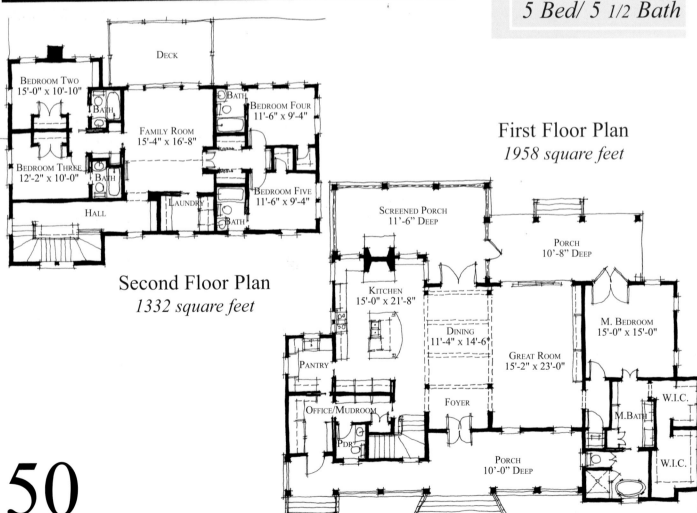

First Floor Plan
1958 square feet

Second Floor Plan
1332 square feet

Second Floor Plan labels:
DECK
BEDROOM TWO 15'-0" x 10'-10"
BATH
BEDROOM THREE 12'-2" x 10'-0"
BATH
FAMILY ROOM 15'-4" x 16'-8"
BATH
BEDROOM FOUR 11'-6" x 9'-4"
BEDROOM FIVE 11'-6" x 9'-4"
BATH
HALL
LAUNDRY

First Floor Plan labels:
SCREENED PORCH 11'-6" DEEP
PORCH 10'-8" DEEP
KITCHEN 15'-0" x 21'-8"
PANTRY
OFFICE/MUDROOM
PDR.
DINING 11'-4" x 14'-6"
GREAT ROOM 15'-2" x 23'-0"
FOYER
M. BEDROOM 15'-0" x 15'-0"
W.I.C.
M.BATH
W.I.C.
PORCH 10'-0" DEEP

50

ALLISON RAMSEY ARCHITECTS INC. • PHONE: 843.986.0559 • ONLINE: www.allisonramseyarchitects.com

ALLISON RAMSEY
Architects *Inc.* creating sustainable timeless design

THE
TANGLEWOOD

*WWW.ALLISONRAMSEYARCHITECTS.COM/
THETANGLEWOOD.PDF*

Identification #
C0551
Heated square feet

2125

Overall Dimensions
41'-6" x 56'-0"

Height to Ridge
29'-4"

3 Bed/ 3 1/2 Bath

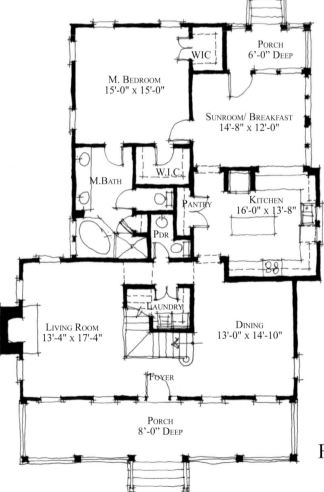

First Floor Plan
1543 square feet

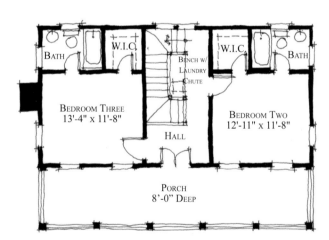

Second Floor Plan
582 square feet

51

ALLISON RAMSEY
Architects *Inc.* creating sustainable timeless design

THE VILLAGE DOUBLE

WWW.ALLISONRAMSEYARCHITECTS.COM/THE VILLAGEDOUBLE.PDF

Identification #
C0552
Heated square feet
1033 *each*
Overall Dimensions
39'-7" x 51'-6"
Height to Ridge
29'-10"

2 Bed/2 Bath each

52

First Floor Plan
621 square feet each

Second Floor Plan
412 square feet each

THE RICHMOND
HILL

WWW.ALLISONRAMSEYARCHITECTS.COM/
RICHMONDHILL.PDF

Identification #
C0553
Heated square feet

2853

Overall Dimensions
64'-4" x 63'-0"

Height to Ridge
24'-8"

3 Bed/ 2 1/2 Bath

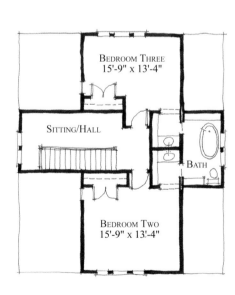

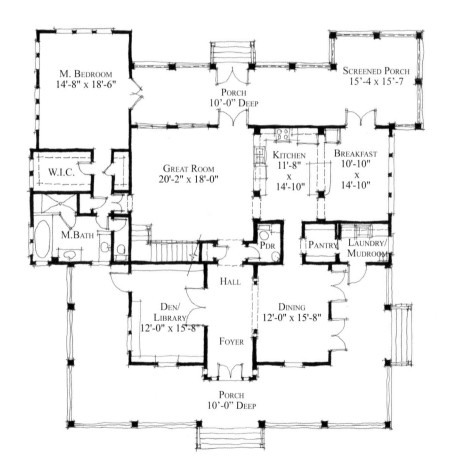

Second Floor Plan
768 square feet

Bedroom Three
15'-9" x 13'-4"

Sitting/Hall

Bath

Bedroom Two
15'-9" x 13'-4"

M. Bedroom
14'-8" x 18'-6"

Porch
10'-0" Deep

Screened Porch
15'-4 x 15'-7

W.I.C.

Great Room
20'-2" x 18'-0"

Kitchen
11'-8"
x
14'-10"

Breakfast
10'-10"
x
14'-10"

M.Bath

Pdr

Pantry

Laundry/
Mudroom

Hall

Den/
Library
12'-0" x 15'-8"

Dining
12'-0" x 15'-8"

Foyer

Porch
10'-0" Deep

First Floor Plan
2085 square feet

53

ALLISON RAMSEY

Architects Inc. creating sustainable timeless design

MARSHVIEW II

*WWW.ALLISONRAMSEYARCHITECTS.COM/
MARSHVIEWII.PDF*

Identification #

C0554

Heated square feet

3711

Overall Dimensions

46'-3" x 80'-10"

Height to Ridge

33'-9"

5 Bed/ 5 Bath

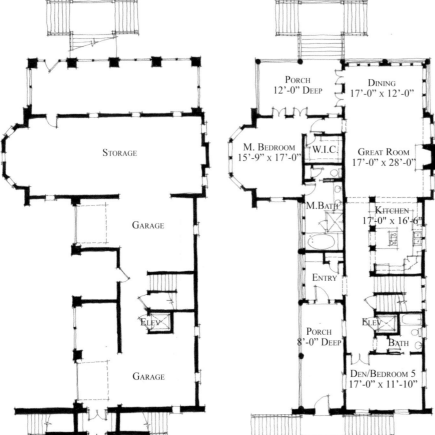

Ground Floor Plan
2485 square feet

First Floor Plan
2007 square feet

Second Floor Plan
1704 square feet

54

WHITERS PLACE

WWW.ALLISONRAMSEYARCHITECTS.COM/
WHITERSPLACE.PDF

Identification #
C0555
Heated square feet

2737

Overall Dimensions
32'-6" x 69'-10"

Height to Ridge
30'-11"

4 Bed/ 4 1/2 Bath

First Floor Plan
1561 square feet

Second Floor Plan
1176 square feet

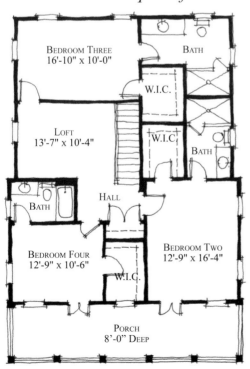

Second Floor Plan labels:
- BEDROOM THREE 16'-10" x 10'-0"
- BATH
- W.I.C.
- LOFT 13'-7" x 10'-4"
- W.I.C.
- BATH
- BATH
- HALL
- BEDROOM FOUR 12'-9" x 10'-6"
- W.I.C.
- BEDROOM TWO 12'-9" x 16'-4"
- PORCH 8'-0" DEEP

First Floor Plan labels:
- SCREENED PORCH 11'-0" DEEP
- M. BEDROOM 14'-4" x 16'-2"
- W.I.C.
- W.I.C.
- BREAKFAST 16'-10" x 8'-4"
- KITCHEN 13'-2" x 13'-6"
- M.BATH
- PANTRY
- PDR
- W.I.C.
- LAUNDRY
- LIVING 18'-2" x 16'-0"
- STUDY/ DINING 12'-4" x 10'-4"
- PORCH 8'-0" DEEP

55

BEACH BUNGALOW

WWW.ALLISONRAMSEYARCHITECTS.COM/
BEACHBUNGALOW.PDF

Identification #
C0556
Heated square feet

1749

Overall Dimensions
34'-0" x 61'-0"

Height to Ridge
24'-7"

3 Bed/ 3 1/2 Bath

First Floor Plan
1209 square feet

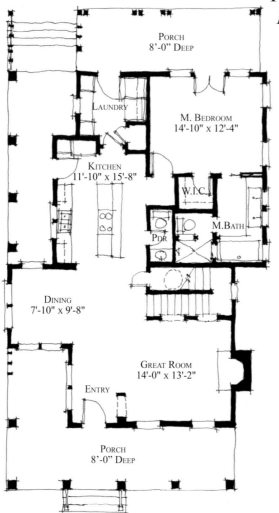

PORCH
8'-0" DEEP

LAUNDRY

M. BEDROOM
14'-10" x 12'-4"

KITCHEN
11'-10" x 15'-8"

W.I.C.

PDR

M.BATH

DINING
7'-10" x 9'-8"

GREAT ROOM
14'-0" x 13'-2"

ENTRY

PORCH
8'-0" DEEP

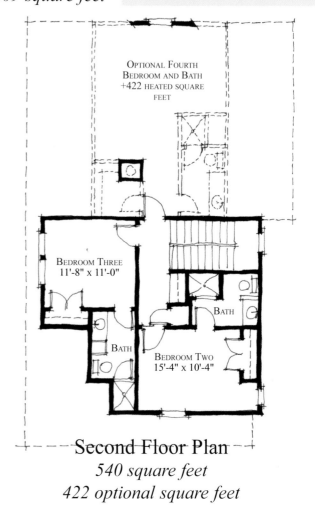

OPTIONAL FOURTH
BEDROOM AND BATH
+422 HEATED SQUARE
FEET

BEDROOM THREE
11'-8" x 11'-0"

BATH

BATH

BEDROOM TWO
15'-4" x 10'-4"

Second Floor Plan
540 square feet
422 optional square feet

56

THE
RIBAUT SQUARE

WWW.ALLISONRAMSEYARCHITECTS.COM/RIB-AUTSQUARE.PDF

Identification #
C0557
Heated square feet
1943
Overall Dimensions
26'-10" x 71'-0"
Height to Ridge
34'-5"

3 Bed/ 3 1/2 Bath

First Floor Plan
1138 square feet

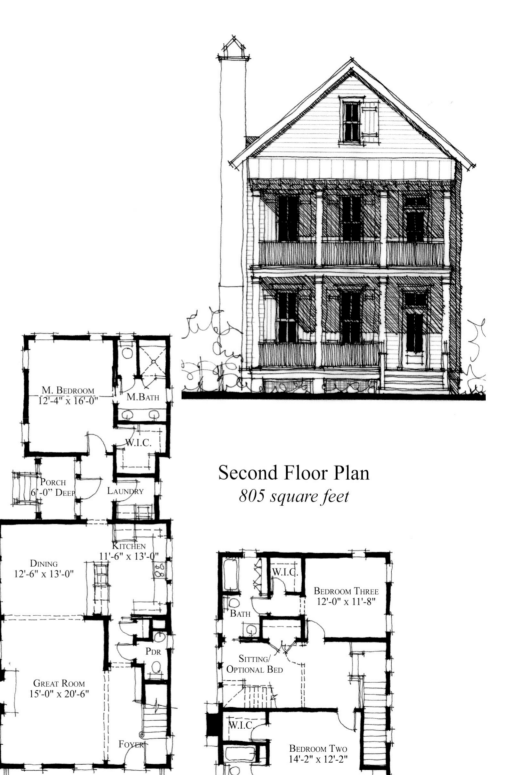

Second Floor Plan
805 square feet

M. BEDROOM
12'-4" x 16'-0"

M.BATH

W.I.C.

PORCH
6'-0" DEEP

LAUNDRY

KITCHEN
11'-6" x 13'-0"

DINING
12'-6" x 13'-0"

PDR

GREAT ROOM
15'-0" x 20'-6"

FOYER

PORCH
10'-0" DEEP

W.I.C.

BATH

BEDROOM THREE
12'-0" x 11'-8"

SITTING/
OPTIONAL BED

W.I.C.

BATH

BEDROOM TWO
14'-2" x 12'-2"

PORCH
10'-0" DEEP

57

ALLISON RAMSEY
Architects Inc. creating sustainable timeless design

THE COOSAW RIVER COTTAGE

WWW.ALLISONRAMSEYARCHITECTS.COM/
THECOOSAWRIVERCOTTAGE.PDF

Identification #
C0030
Heated square feet

1709 *without optional*

Overall Dimensions
32'-4" x 60'-4"

Height to Ridge
26'-5"

3 Bed/ 21/2 Bath

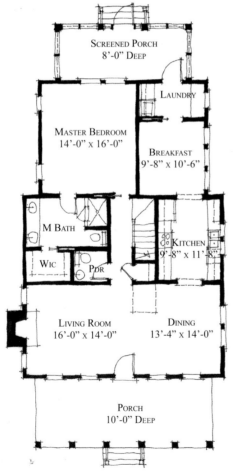

First Floor Plan
1195 square feet

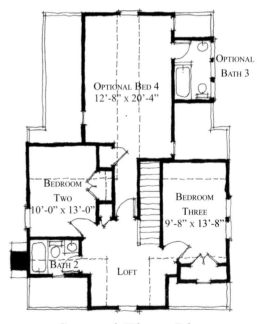

Second Floor Plan
514 square feet
360 optional square feet

ALLISON RAMSEY

Architects Inc. creating sustainable timeless design

THE COOSAW RIVER COTTAGE. A

solid performer, the Coosaw River Cottage has proven itself in many of the best neighborhoods in the southeast; Habersham, Newpoint, Hammonds Ferry, and Watercolor to name a few. This cottage has it all. Packed into a footprint that is small lot friendly, this cottage lives large. Three Bedrooms with a Master Suite on the first floor, an open and casual floorplan, a very livable front porch and a more private screened rear porch are a few of the elements that make this house so popular. Since first publishing this plan in our Volume I planbook we have adapted the plan to provide the option for an optional Fourth Bedroom and Third Bath upstairs.

59

ALLISON RAMSEY

Architects Inc. creating sustainable timeless design

SHELL POINT QUARTERS

WWW.ALLISONRAMSEYARCHITECTS.COM/
SHELLPOINTQUARTERS.PDF

Identification #
C0560
Heated square feet
1263
Overall Dimensions
28'-6" x 36'-2"
Height to Ridge
21'-6"

2 Bed/ 2 1/2 Bath

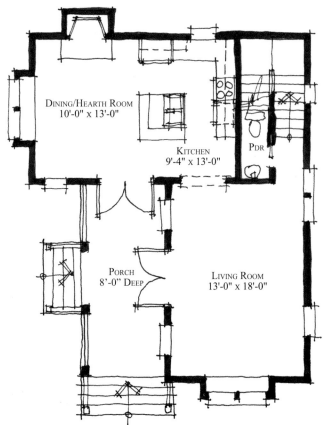

DINING/HEARTH ROOM
10'-0" x 13'-0"

KITCHEN
9'-4" x 13'-0"

PDR

PORCH
8'-0" DEEP

LIVING ROOM
13'-0" x 18'-0"

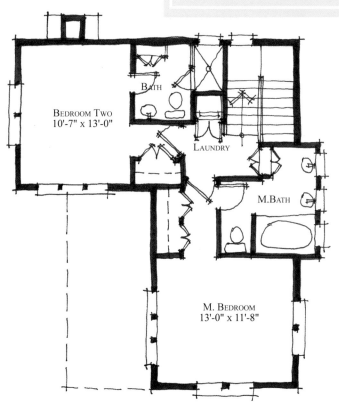

BATH

BEDROOM TWO
10'-7" x 13'-0"

LAUNDRY

M.BATH

M. BEDROOM
13'-0" x 11'-8"

60

First Floor Plan
668 square feet

Second Floor Plan
595 square feet

ALLISON RAMSEY
Architects *Inc.* creating sustainable timeless design

FIDDLER'S TOWER

WWW.ALLISONRAMSEYARCHITECTS.COM/FID-DLERSTOWER.PDF

Identification #
C0561
Heated square feet

2842

Overall Dimensions
35'-5" x 61'-4"

Height to Ridge
33'-11"

4 Bed/ 4 1/2 Bath

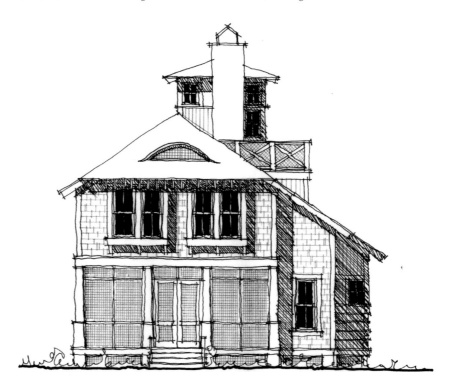

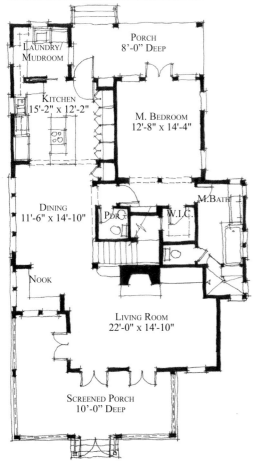

LAUNDRY/ MUDROOM

PORCH 8'-0" DEEP

KITCHEN 15'-2" x 12'-2"

M. BEDROOM 12'-8" x 14'-4"

DINING 11'-6" x 14'-10"

PDR

W.I.C.

M.BATH

NOOK

LIVING ROOM 22'-0" x 14'-10"

SCREENED PORCH 10'-0" DEEP

First Floor Plan
1387 square feet

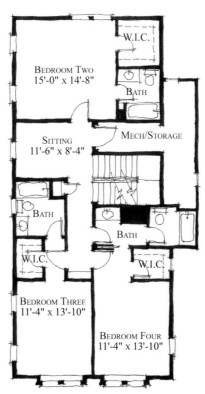

W.I.C.

BEDROOM TWO 15'-0" x 14'-8"

BATH

MECH/STORAGE

SITTING 11'-6" x 8'-4"

BATH

BATH

W.I.C.

W.I.C.

BEDROOM THREE 11'-4" x 13'-10"

BEDROOM FOUR 11'-4" x 13'-10"

Second Floor Plan
1377 square feet

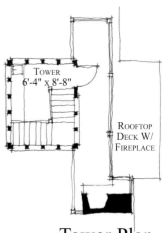

TOWER 6'-4" x 8'-8"

ROOFTOP DECK W/ FIREPLACE

Tower Plan
78 square feet

61

ARA
ALLISON RAMSEY
creating sustainable timeless design

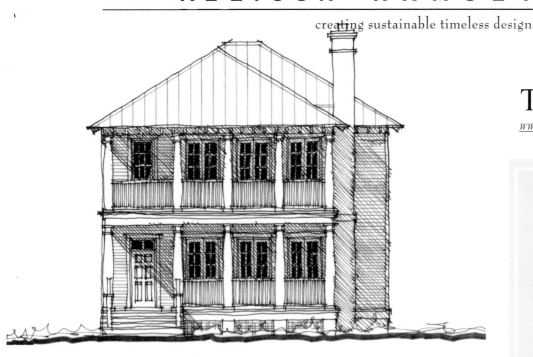

THE GULFSIDE

WWW.ALLISONRAMSEYARCHITECTS.COM/
THEGULFSIDE.PDF

Identification #
C0562
Heated square feet
1997
Overall Dimensions
33'-0" x 59'-4"
Height to Ridge
29'-5"

4 Bed/ 3 Bath

First Floor Plan
1022 square feet

Second Floor Plan
975 square feet

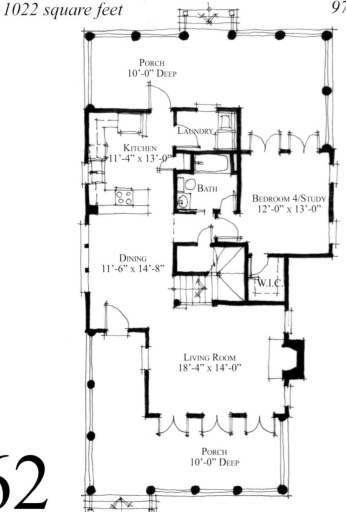

PORCH 10'-0" DEEP

LAUNDRY

KITCHEN 11'-4" x 13'-0"

BATH

BEDROOM 4/STUDY 12'-0" x 13'-0"

DINING 11'-6" x 14'-8"

W.I.C.

LIVING ROOM 18'-4" x 14'-0"

PORCH 10'-0" DEEP

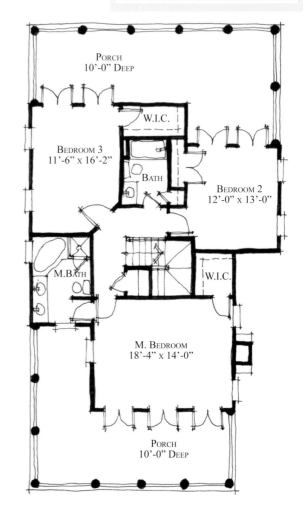

PORCH 10'-0" DEEP

W.I.C.

BEDROOM 3 11'-6" x 16'-2"

BATH

BEDROOM 2 12'-0" x 13'-0"

M.BATH

W.I.C.

M. BEDROOM 18'-4" x 14'-0"

PORCH 10'-0" DEEP

62

VILLAGE JEWEL

WWW.ALLISONRAMSEYARCHITECTS.COM/VIL-LAGEJEWEL.PDF

Identification #
C0563
Heated square feet

982

Overall Dimensions
18'-2" x 53'-8"

Height to Ridge
23'-8"

2 Bed/ 2 Bath

First Floor Plan
716 square feet

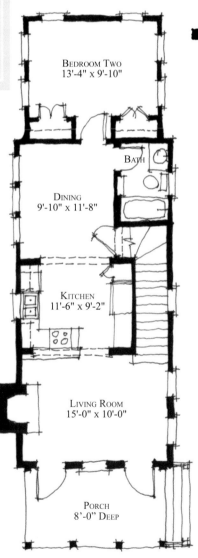

BEDROOM TWO
13'-4" x 9'-10"

BATH

DINING
9'-10" x 11'-8"

KITCHEN
11'-6" x 9'-2"

LIVING ROOM
15'-0" x 10'-0"

PORCH
8'-0" DEEP

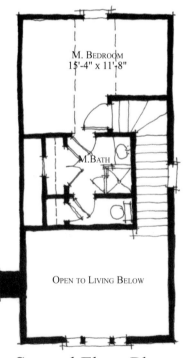

M. BEDROOM
15'-4" x 11'-8"

M. BATH

OPEN TO LIVING BELOW

Second Floor Plan
266 square feet

63

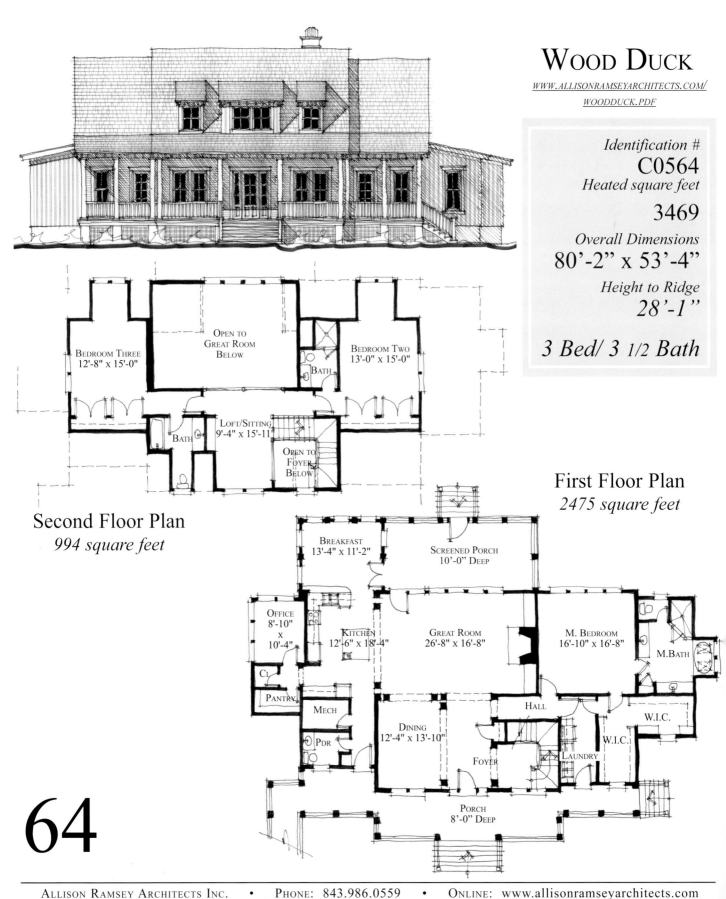

Wood Duck

WWW.ALLISONRAMSEYARCHITECTS.COM/
WOODDUCK.PDF

Identification #
C0564
Heated square feet

3469

Overall Dimensions
80'-2" x 53'-4"

Height to Ridge
28'-1"

3 Bed/ 3 1/2 Bath

Second Floor Plan
994 square feet

BEDROOM THREE
12'-8" x 15'-0"

OPEN TO GREAT ROOM BELOW

BEDROOM TWO
13'-0" x 15'-0"

BATH

BATH

LOFT/SITTING
9'-4" x 15'-11"

OPEN TO FOYER BELOW

First Floor Plan
2475 square feet

BREAKFAST
13'-4" x 11'-2"

SCREENED PORCH
10'-0" Deep

OFFICE
8'-10" x 10'-4"

KITCHEN
12'-6" x 18'-4"

GREAT ROOM
26'-8" x 16'-8"

M. BEDROOM
16'-10" x 16'-8"

M.BATH

CL

PANTRY

MECH

HALL

W.I.C.

W.I.C.

PDR

DINING
12'-4" x 13'-10"

FOYER

LAUNDRY

PORCH
8'-0" Deep

64

ALLISON RAMSEY
Architects Inc. *creating sustainable timeless design*

PALMETTO BLUFF
RIVER HOUSE

*WWW.ALLISONRAMSEYARCHITECTS.COM/PAL-
METTOBLUFFRIVERHOUSE.PDF*

Identification #
C0565
Heated square feet

3814

Overall Dimensions
74'-8" x 58'-0"

Height to Ridge
34'-4"

5 Bed/ 4 1/2 Bath

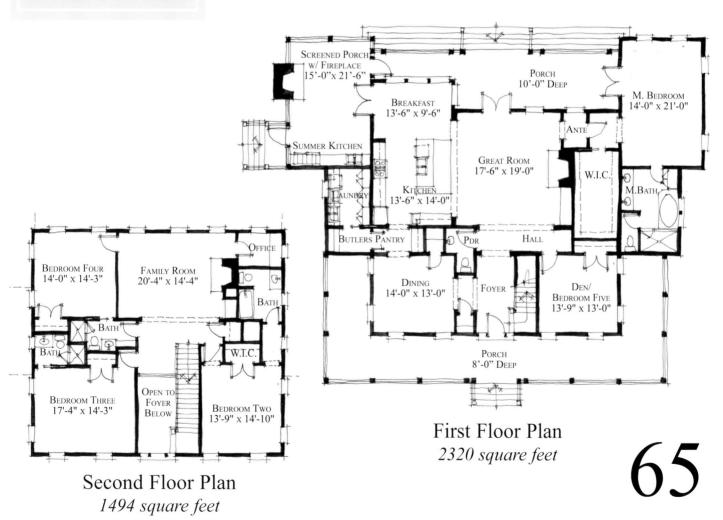

First Floor Plan
2320 square feet

Second Floor Plan
1494 square feet

65

ALLISON RAMSEY
Architects *Inc.* creating sustainable timeless design

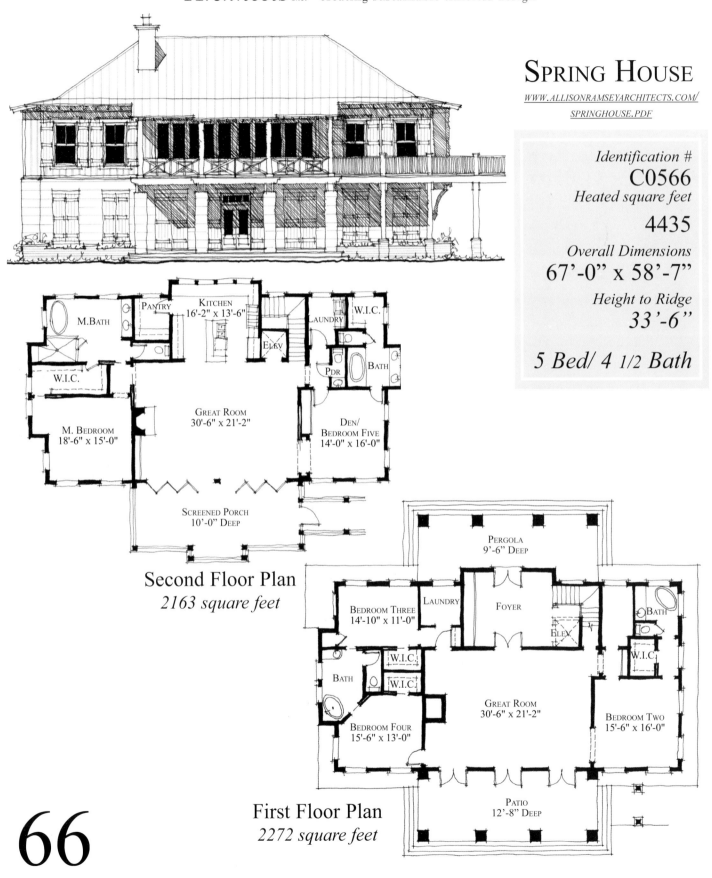

Spring House

WWW.ALLISONRAMSEYARCHITECTS.COM/
SPRINGHOUSE.PDF

Identification #

C0566
Heated square feet

4435

Overall Dimensions
67'-0" x 58'-7"

Height to Ridge
33'-6"

5 Bed/ 4 1/2 Bath

Second Floor Plan
2163 square feet

First Floor Plan
2272 square feet

66

ALLISON RAMSEY
Architects Inc. creating sustainable timeless design

THE MOUNT PLEASANT

WWW.ALLISONRAMSEYARCHITECTS.COM/
THEMOUNPLEASANT.PDF

Identification #
C0567
Heated square feet

4406

Overall Dimensions
87'-8" x 58'-0"

Height to Ridge
30'-4"

4 Bed/ 4 1/2 Bath

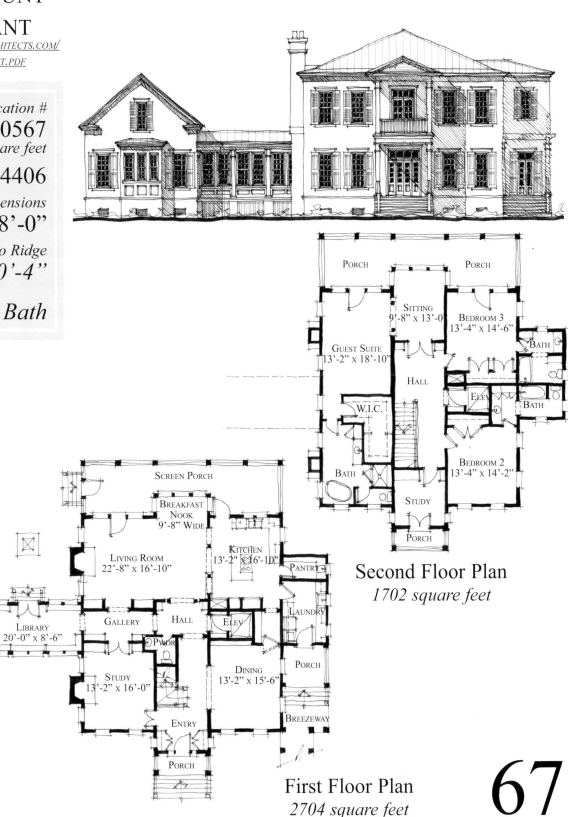

Second Floor Plan
1702 square feet

First Floor Plan
2704 square feet

67

ALLISON RAMSEY

Architects Inc. creating sustainable timeless design

WHISPER CREEK
COTTAGE

WWW.ALLISONRAMSEYARCHITECTS.COM/
WHISPERCREEKCOTTAGE.PDF

Identification #
C0568
Heated square feet
1554
Overall Dimensions
43'-0" x 59'-0"
Height to Ridge
23'-0"

2 Bed/ 2 1/2 Bath

PORCH
8'-0" DEEP

BEDROOM TWO
11'-6" x 12'-0"

M. BEDROOM
14'-6" x 14'-8"

BATH

DINING/ LIBRARY
11'-6" x 12'-4"

PDR

W.I.C.

LAUNDRY

PANTRY

M.BATH

GREAT ROOM
19'-10" x 17'-0"

KITCHEN
8'-6" x 17'-0"

PORCH
8'-0" DEEP

First Floor Plan
1554 square feet

ARA
ALLISON RAMSEY
Architects Inc. creating sustainable timeless design

THE WHISPER CREEK COTTAGE

is that perfect cottage that everyone dreams of. Perfect for a mountain getaway, a beach house, a retreat on the river, or a great house for a new or downsizing family. This Cottage has a rural vernacular aesthetic shaped by it's low pitched roofs, generous porches, and traditional materials. The Whisper Creek is more than just a pretty face, boasting an open floor plan, two bedrooms, and an abundance of outdoor living space on the porches.

THE WHISPER CREEK IS THE 2009 SOUTHERN LIVING GIVE-AWAY HOUSE WINNER.

69

ARA

ALLISON RAMSEY

Architects Inc. creating sustainable timeless design

GLOUCESTER POINT

WWW.ALLISONRAMSEYARCHITECTS.COM/
GLOUCESTERPOINT.PDF

Identification #
C0570
Heated square feet

2734

Overall Dimensions
25'-0" x 60'-0"

Height to Ridge
42'-11"

4 Bed/3 1/2 Bath

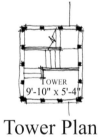

Tower Plan
54 square feet

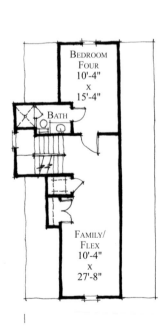

BEDROOM FOUR 10'-4" x 15'-4"

BATH

FAMILY/ FLEX 10'-4" x 27'-8"

PORCH 8'-0" DEEP

M. BEDROOM 22'-0" x 15'-4"

W.I.C.

M. BATH

BATH

LAUNDRY

BEDROOM TWO 12'-0" x 10'-2"

BEDROOM THREE 10'-0" x 14'-0"

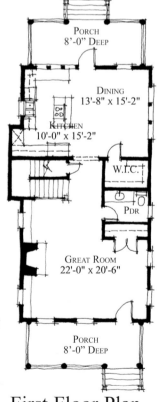

PORCH 8'-0" DEEP

DINING 13'-8" x 15'-2"

KITCHEN 10'-0" x 15'-2"

W.I.C.

PDR

GREAT ROOM 22'-0" x 20'-6"

PORCH 8'-0" DEEP

70

Loft Plan
606 square feet

Second Floor Plan
1037 square feet

First Floor Plan
1037 square feet

ALLISON RAMSEY
Architects Inc.   creating sustainable timeless design

COLLINS CREEK
GUEST AND GARAGE

WWW.ALLISONRAMSEYARCHITECTS.COM/
COLLINSCREEKGUESTANDGARAGE.PDF

Identification #
C0571
Heated square feet
756

Overall Dimensions
26'-0" x 42'-5"

Height to Ridge
33'-6"

2 Bed/ 1 Bath

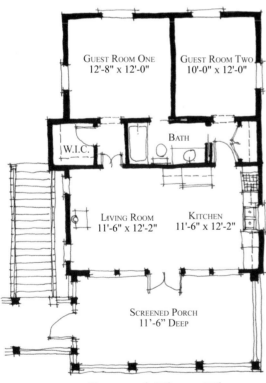

GUEST ROOM ONE
12'-8" x 12'-0"

GUEST ROOM TWO
10'-0" x 12'-0"

BATH

W.I.C.

LIVING ROOM
11'-6" x 12'-2"

KITCHEN
11'-6" x 12'-2"

SCREENED PORCH
11'-6" DEEP

Second Floor Plan
756 square feet

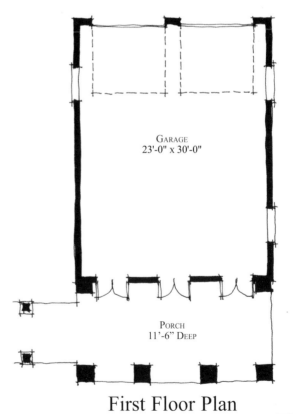

GARAGE
23'-0" x 30'-0"

PORCH
11'-6" DEEP

First Floor Plan
762 square feet

71

ALLISON RAMSEY
Architects Inc. creating sustainable timeless design

THE BEACH BARN

WWW.ALLISONRAMSEYARCHITECTS.COM/
THEBEACHBARN.PDF

Identification #
C0572
Heated square feet

2377

Overall Dimensions
38'-0" x 66'-8"

Height to Ridge
33'-4"

4 Bed/ 4 Bath

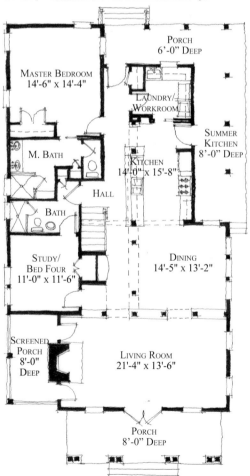

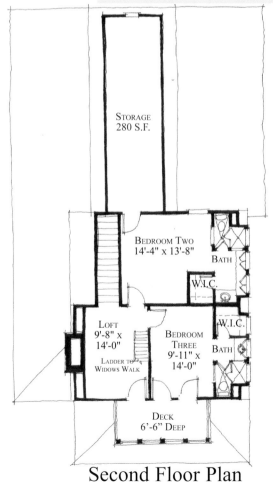

72

First Floor Plan
1719 square feet

Second Floor Plan
658 square feet

POOL SIDE
HIDEOUT

WWW.ALLISONRAMSEYARCHITECTS.COM/
POOLSIDEHIDEOUT.PDF

Identification #

C0573

Heated square feet

920

Overall Dimensions

30'-0" x 34'-0"

Height to Ridge

24'-9"

1 Bed/ 2 Bath

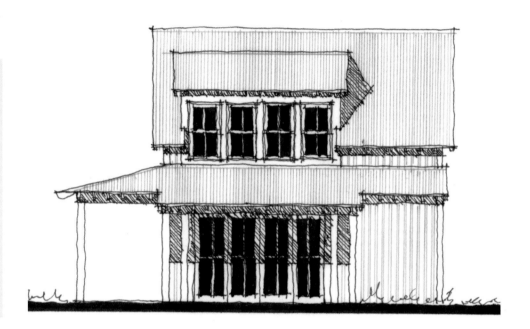

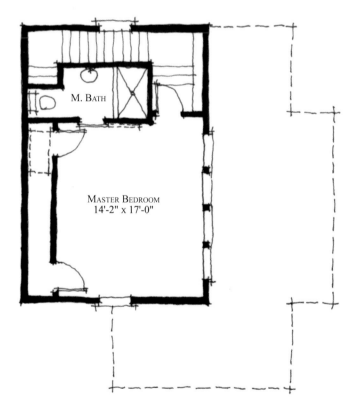

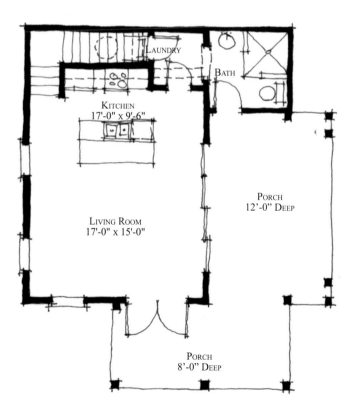

Second Floor Plan
388 square feet

First Floor Plan
532 square feet

73

ARA
ALLISON RAMSEY
Architects Inc. creating sustainable timeless design

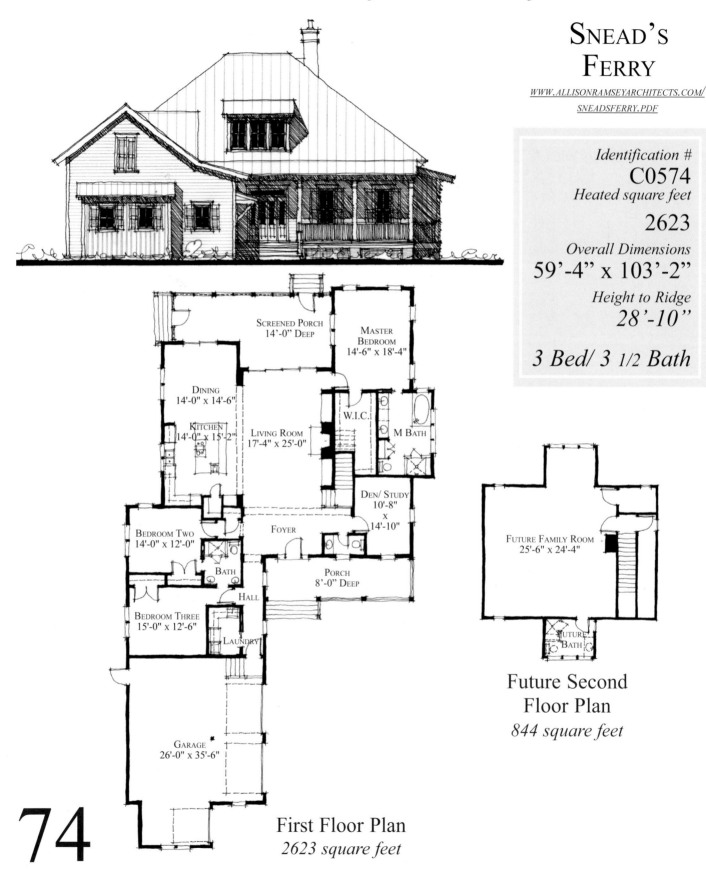

SNEAD'S FERRY

WWW.ALLISONRAMSEYARCHITECTS.COM/
SNEADSFERRY.PDF

Identification #
C0574
Heated square feet
2623

Overall Dimensions
59'-4" x 103'-2"

Height to Ridge
28'-10"

3 Bed/ 3 1/2 Bath

SCREENED PORCH
14'-0" DEEP

MASTER
BEDROOM
14'-6" x 18'-4"

DINING
14'-0" x 14'-6"

KITCHEN
14'-0" x 15'-2"

W.I.C.

LIVING ROOM
17'-4" x 25'-0"

M BATH

DEN/ STUDY
10'-8"
x
14'-10"

FUTURE FAMILY ROOM
25'-6" x 24'-4"

BEDROOM TWO
14'-0" x 12'-0"

FOYER

BATH

PORCH
8'-0" DEEP

FUTURE
BATH

HALL

BEDROOM THREE
15'-0" x 12'-6"

LAUNDRY

Future Second
Floor Plan
844 square feet

GARAGE
26'-0" x 35'-6"

74

First Floor Plan
2623 square feet

ARSENAL HILL

WWW.ALLISONRAMSEYARCHITECTS.COM/
ARSENALHILL.PDF

Identification #
C0575
Heated square feet
1568
Overall Dimensions
35'-0" x 64'-5"

Height to Ridge
18'-8"

3 Bed/ 2 Bath

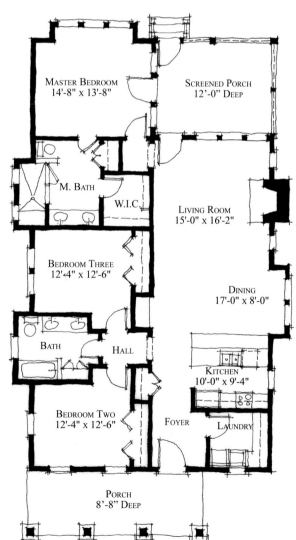

MASTER BEDROOM
14'-8" x 13'-8"

SCREENED PORCH
12'-0" Deep

M. BATH

W.I.C.

LIVING ROOM
15'-0" x 16'-2"

BEDROOM THREE
12'-4" x 12'-6"

DINING
17'-0" x 8'-0"

BATH

HALL

KITCHEN
10'-0" x 9'-4"

First Floor Plan
1568 square feet

BEDROOM TWO
12'-4" x 12'-6"

FOYER

LAUNDRY

PORCH
8'-8" Deep

75

A R A
ALLISON RAMSEY
Architects Inc. creating sustainable timeless design

CRACKER COTTAGE

WWW.ALLISONRAMSEYARCHITECTS.COM/
CRACKERCOTTAGE.PDF

Identification #
C0576
Heated square feet
1744
Overall Dimensions
48'-4" x 54'-0"
Height to Ridge
21'-4"

3 Bed/ 2 Bath

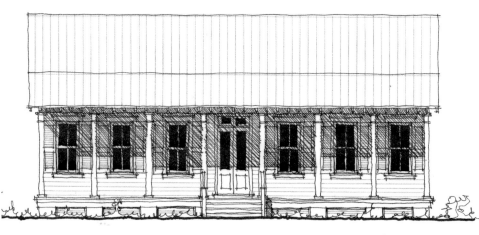

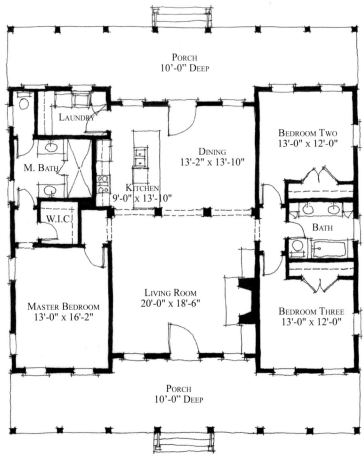

PORCH
10'-0" DEEP

LAUNDRY

BEDROOM TWO
13'-0" x 12'-0"

M. BATH

DINING
13'-2" x 13'-10"

KITCHEN
9'-0" x 13'-10"

BATH

W.I.C.

MASTER BEDROOM
13'-0" x 16'-2"

LIVING ROOM
20'-0" x 18'-6"

BEDROOM THREE
13'-0" x 12'-0"

PORCH
10'-0" DEEP

76

First Floor Plan
1744 square feet

GOLF COTTAGE

WWW.ALLISONRAMSEYARCHITECTS.COM/
GOLFCOTTAGE.PDF

Identification #
C0577
Heated square feet

994

Overall Dimensions
37'-0" x 47'-8"

Height to Ridge
22'-2"

2 Bed/ 2 Bath

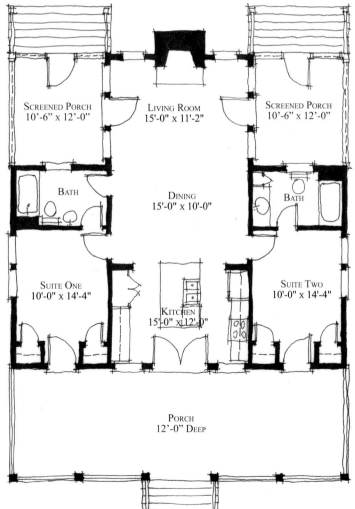

SCREENED PORCH
10'-6" x 12'-0"

LIVING ROOM
15'-0" x 11'-2"

SCREENED PORCH
10'-6" x 12'-0"

BATH

DINING
15'-0" x 10'-0"

BATH

SUITE ONE
10'-0" x 14'-4"

KITCHEN
15'-0" x 12'-0"

SUITE TWO
10'-0" x 14'-4"

PORCH
12'-0" DEEP

First Floor Plan
994 square feet

77

ARA
ALLISON RAMSEY
Architects Inc. creating sustainable timeless design

BERMUDA
BLUFF COTTAGE

WWW.ALLISONRAMSEYARCHITECTS.COM/
BERMUDABLUFFCOTTAGE.PDF

Identification #
C0002
Heated square feet

2003

Overall Dimensions
54'-8" x 50'-8"

Height to Ridge
26'-2"

3 Bed/ 3 Bath

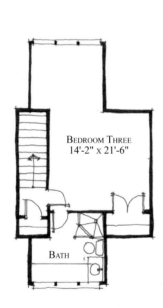

Second Floor Plan
397 square feet

First Floor Plan
1606 square feet

ALLISON RAMSEY
Architects Inc. creating sustainable timeless design

BERMUDA BLUFF

has been called iconic, quintes-
cential, and perfect by many and
it's popularity has supported these
claims. The Bermuda Bluff is a solid
interpretation of the rural lowcountry
cottage. Containing a Master Suite
and second bed and bath downstairs,
generous porches, and open floor
plan it is the perfect cottage for a
family, downsizers, retirees, or even a
getaway destination.

RENDERING FROM SOUTHERN LIVING PUBLICATIONS

THE BERMUDA BLUFF
WAS THE 1998 HGTV
DREAM HOUSE. IT HAS
ALSO CONSISTANTLY BEEN
A SOUTHERN LIVING
HOME PLANS TOP SELLER
AS WELL AS AN ALLISON
RAMSEY TOP SELLER.

79

ALLISON RAMSEY
Architects *Inc.* creating sustainable timeless design

RIVER CAMP

WWW.ALLISONRAMSEYARCHITECTS.COM/RIVERCAMP.PDF

Identification #
C0580
Heated square feet

1534

Overall Dimensions
47'-0" x 55'-2"

Height to Ridge
20'-4"

3 Bed/ 2 Bath

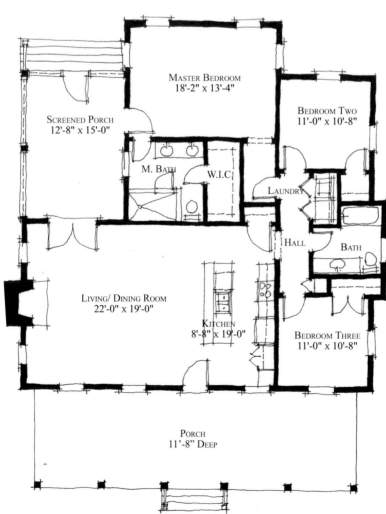

MASTER BEDROOM
18'-2" x 13'-4"

SCREENED PORCH
12'-8" x 15'-0"

BEDROOM TWO
11'-0" x 10'-8"

M. BATH

W.I.C

LAUNDRY

HALL

BATH

LIVING/ DINING ROOM
22'-0" x 19'-0"

KITCHEN
8'-8" x 19'-0"

BEDROOM THREE
11'-0" x 10'-8"

PORCH
11'-8" Deep

80

First Floor Plan
1534 square feet

A R A
ALLISON RAMSEY
Architects Inc. creating sustainable timeless design

PRITCHARDS

WWW.ALLISONRAMSEYARCHITECTS.COM/
PRITCHARDS.PDF

Identification #
C0581
Heated square feet

3811

Overall Dimensions
37'-4" x 81'-0"

Height to Ridge
30'-9"

4 Bed/ 3 1/2 Bath

Second Floor Plan
1886 square feet

PORCH
8'-0" DEEP

M SITTING
7'-10" x 16'-8"

MASTER BEDROOM
15'-0" x 16'-8"

W.I.C.

M. BATH

L

W.I.C.

ELEV

BEDROOM TWO
11'-2" x 12'-2"

LAUNDRY

W.I.C.

BATH

BATH

W.I.C.

W.I.C.

BEDROOM FOUR
14'-8" x 11'-10"

HALL

BEDROOM THREE
14'-8" x 11'-10"

PORCH
8'-0" DEEP

First Floor Plan
1925 square feet

PORCH
8'-0" DEEP

FAMILY ROOM
13'-0" x 22'-2"

KITCHEN
10'-0" x 22'-2"

BUTLERS
PANTRY

ELEV

LIVING ROOM
20'-6" x 22'-10"

OFFICE/ENTRY
11'-0" x 8'-10"

PDR

DINING
12'-8" x 13'-0"

FOYER

STUDY
12'-10" x 10'-8"

PORCH
8'-0" DEEP

81

Garage Plan Included

ARA
ALLISON RAMSEY
Architects Inc. creating sustainable timeless design

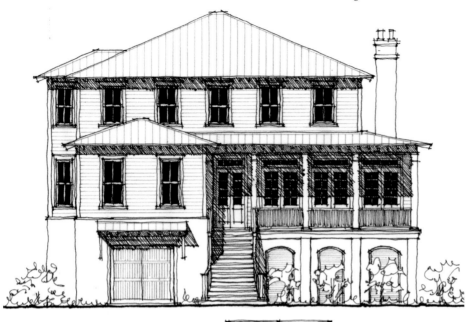

FRIPP RETREAT

WWW.ALLISONRAMSEYARCHITECTS.COM/
FRIPPRETREAT.PDF

Identification #
C0582
Heated square feet
3843
Overall Dimensions
52'-0" x 96'-8"
Height to Ridge
29'-4"

6 Bed/ 6 1/2 Bath

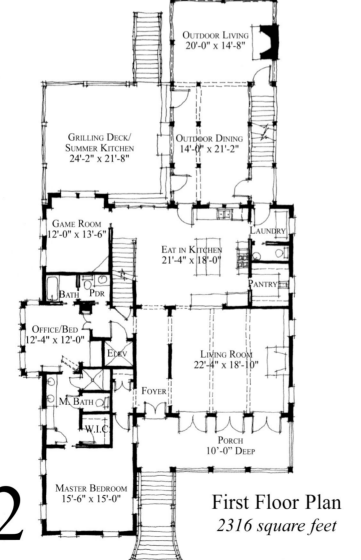

OUTDOOR LIVING
20'-0" x 14'-8"

GRILLING DECK/
SUMMER KITCHEN
24'-2" x 21'-8"

OUTDOOR DINING
14'-0" x 21'-2"

LAUNDRY

GAME ROOM
12'-0" x 13'-6"

EAT IN KITCHEN
21'-4" x 18'-0"

PANTRY

BATH PDR

OFFICE/BED
12'-4" x 12'-0"

ELEV

LIVING ROOM
22'-4" x 18'-10"

M. BATH

FOYER

W.I.C.

PORCH
10'-0" Deep

MASTER BEDROOM
15'-6" x 15'-0"

First Floor Plan
2316 square feet

PARTY DECK
20'-0" x 15'-8"

Second Floor Plan
1527 square feet

BEDROOM
THREE
12'-2" x
14'-8"

W.I.C.

FAMILY ROOM
21'-10" x 15'-0"

BATH

BATH BATH

BEDROOM
FOUR
12'-6" x
12'-4"

ELEV

LAUNDRY

BATH

BUNK ROOM

BEDROOM FIVE
14'-10" x 14'-1"

82

Garage Plan Included

BEAUFORT
RIVER COTTAGE

WWW.ALLISONRAMSEYARCHITECTS.COM/
BEAUFORTRIVERCOTTAGE.PDF

Identification #
C0583
Heated square feet

1022

Overall Dimensions
30'-0" x 44'-2"

Height to Ridge
17'-5"

2 Bed/ 2 Bath

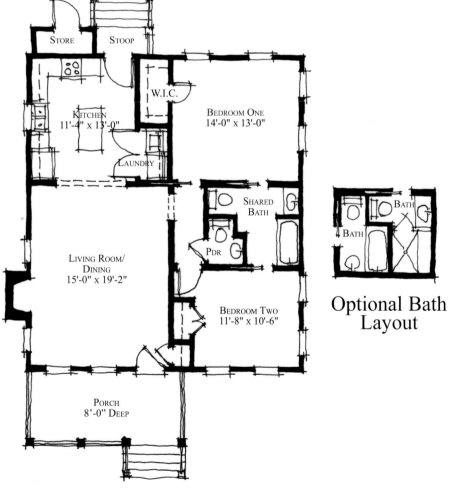

STORE STOOP

W.I.C.

KITCHEN
11'-4" x 13'-0"

BEDROOM ONE
14'-0" x 13'-0"

LAUNDRY

SHARED
BATH

PDR

LIVING ROOM/
DINING
15'-0" x 19'-2"

BEDROOM TWO
11'-8" x 10'-6"

BATH

BATH

Optional Bath
Layout

PORCH
8'-0" Deep

First Floor Plan
1022 square feet

83

ALLISON RAMSEY

creating sustainable timeless design

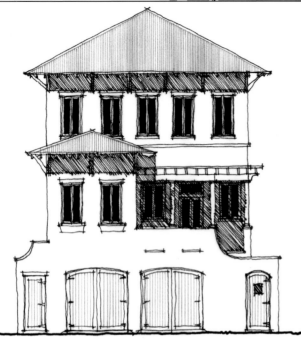

FACTORY CREEK

WWW.ALLISONRAMSEYARCHITECTS.COM/
FACTORYCREEK.PDF

Identification #
C0584
Heated square feet

3233

Overall Dimensions
35'-0" x 64'-0"

Height to Ridge
41'-8"

3 Bed/ 3 1/2 Bath

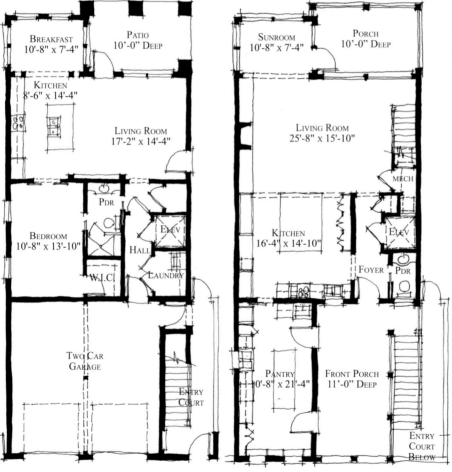

Second Floor Plan
1050 square feet

84

Ground Floor Plan
959 square feet
Garage not included in s.f.

First Floor Plan
1224 square feet

*Garage Plan Included

A R A
ALLISON RAMSEY
Architects Inc. creating sustainable timeless design

THE
OGELTHORPE

WWW.ALLISONRAMSEYARCHITECTS.COM/
THEOGELTHORPE.PDF

Identification #
C0585
Heated square feet
2429
Overall Dimensions
48'-8" x 56'-6"
Height to Ridge
27'-8"

3 Bed/ 3 1/2 Bath

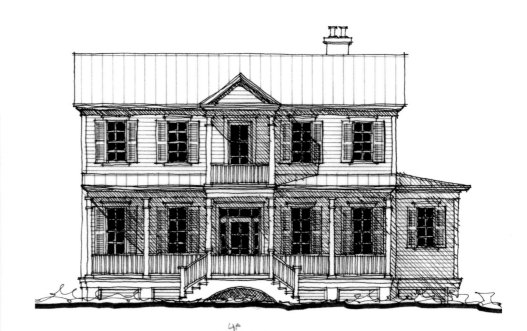

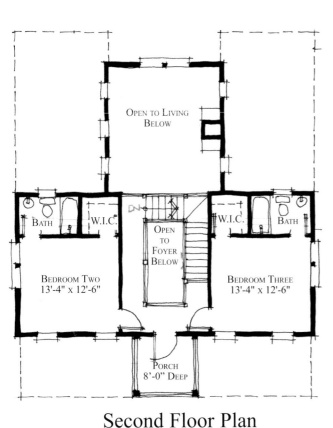

Second Floor Plan
643 square feet

Open to Living Below

Open to Foyer Below

BATH   W.I.C.   W.I.C.   BATH

BEDROOM TWO
13'-4" x 12'-6"

BEDROOM THREE
13'-4" x 12'-6"

PORCH
8'-0" DEEP

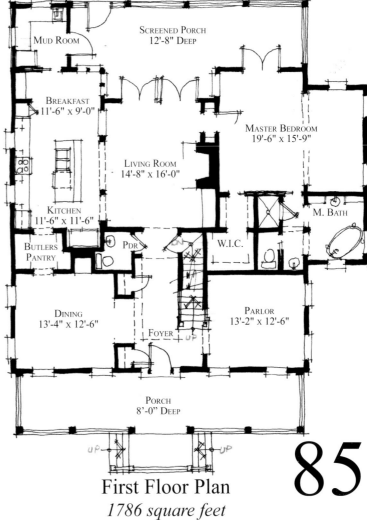

MUD ROOM

SCREENED PORCH
12'-8" DEEP

BREAKFAST
11'-6" x 9'-0"

MASTER BEDROOM
19'-6" x 15'-9"

LIVING ROOM
14'-8" x 16'-0"

KITCHEN
11'-6" x 11'-6"

M. BATH

BUTLERS
PANTRY

PDR

W.I.C.

DINING
13'-4" x 12'-6"

PARLOR
13'-2" x 12'-6"

FOYER

PORCH
8'-0" DEEP

85

First Floor Plan
1786 square feet

ALLISON RAMSEY
Architects Inc. creating sustainable timeless design

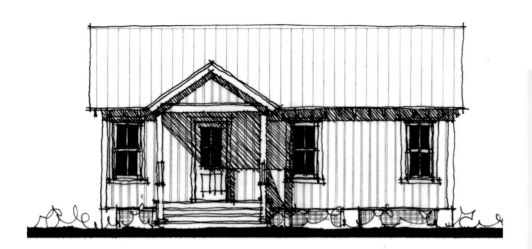

SATILLA RIVER CAMP

WWW.ALLISONRAMSEYARCHITECTS.COM/
SATILLARIVERCAMP.PDF

Identification #

C0586
Heated square feet

656

Overall Dimensions
32'-4" x 31'-4"

Height to Ridge
15'-8"

1 Bed/ 1 Bath

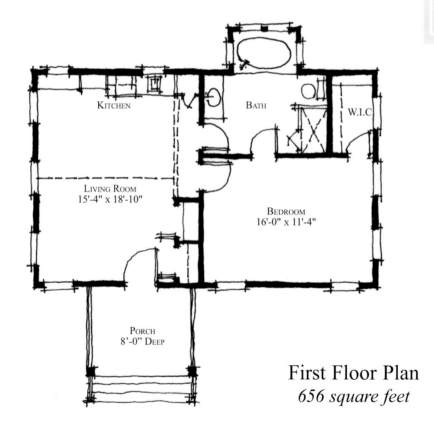

KITCHEN

BATH

W.I.C

LIVING ROOM
15'-4" x 18'-10"

BEDROOM
16'-0" x 11'-4"

PORCH
8'-0" DEEP

First Floor Plan
656 square feet

86

ALLISON RAMSEY

Architects Inc. creating sustainable timeless design

MOUNTAIN LAUREL

WWW.ALLISONRAMSEYARCHITECTS.COM/
MOUNTAINLAUREL.PDF

Identification #
C0587
Heated square feet
3696

Overall Dimensions
80'-8" x 63'-8"

Height to Ridge
32'-10"

4 Bed/ 3 1/2 Bath

*Basement Plan Available

PORCH 12'-8" DEEP

PORCH 12'-8" DEEP

MASTER BEDROOM 16'-0" x 15'-4"

GREAT ROOM 22'-6" x 19'-8"

KITCHEN 14'-6" x 15'-2"

FAMILY/BREAKFAST 16'-8" x 21'-4"

W.I.C.

W.I.C.

ELEV

PDR

LAUNDRY AT MASTER CLOSET

M. BATH

STUDY 15'-0" x 10'-0"

FOYER

DINING 15'-0" x 13'-6"

PORCH 14'-0" DEEP

First Floor Plan
2384 square feet

BEDROOM TWO 16'-0" x 13'-0"

OPEN TO GREAT ROOM BELOW

BEDROOM THREE 19'-6" x 12'-6"

W.I.C.

OPEN HALL

ELEV BATH

OPEN TO FOYER BELOW

W.I.C.

LAUNDRY

BEDROOM FOUR 15'-0" x 10'-6"

SHARED BATH

Second Floor Plan
1312 square feet

87

ALLISON RAMSEY
Architects Inc. creating sustainable timeless design

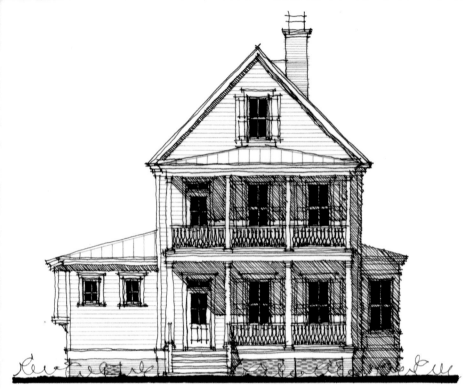

THE PARKSIDE

WWW.ALLISONRAMSEYARCHITECTS.COM/
THEPARKSIDE.PDF

Identification #
C0588
Heated square feet
3145
Overall Dimensions
41'-3" x 73'-0"
Height to Ridge
35'-0"

4 Bed/ 4 1/2 Bath

Second Floor Plan
1125 square feet

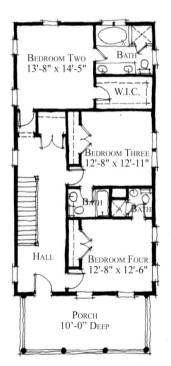

First Floor Plan
2020 square feet

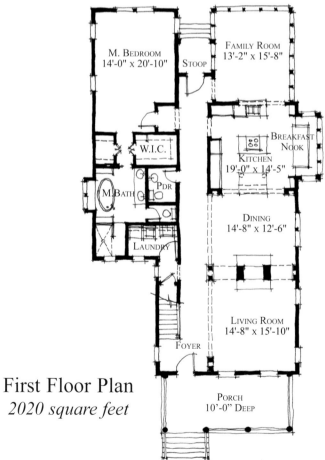

ALLISON RAMSEY

Architects Inc.   creating sustainable timeless design

THE PARKSIDE combines a classic southern double porched exterior with a modern open floor plan bathed in natural light throughout every room. The Kitchen, Dining and Living Room greet each other with open arms and a cozy Breakfast Nook and sunroom complete the more public realm of the house. This is a house built for entertaining. The Parkside is a solid floor plan for todays market with a generous Master Bedroom Suite on the main floor, a second Master and two additional bedrooms and bathrooms upstairs. This plan is a superb choice for a corner lot in a neighborhood setting or a great house for a more rural site with big views.

HOUSE SHOWN IN PHOTOS HAS BEEN ALTERED FROM PLANS.

THE PARKSIDE WAS SELECTED AS A 2008 BEST IN AMERICAN LIVING AWARD WINNER.

89

ARA
ALLISON RAMSEY
Architects *Inc.* creating sustainable timeless design

OLD OYSTER RETREAT

WWW.ALLISONRAMSEYARCHITECTS.COM/
OLDOYSTERRETREAT.PDF

Identification #
C0590
Heated square feet

3968

Overall Dimensions
68'-8" x 67'-2"

Height to Ridge
28'-8"

3 Bed/ 4 1/2 Bath

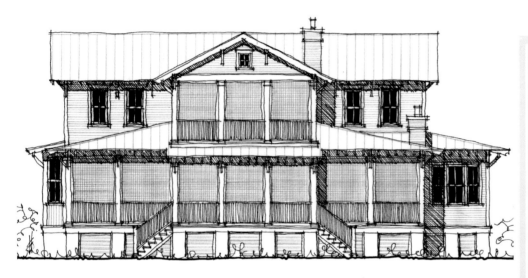

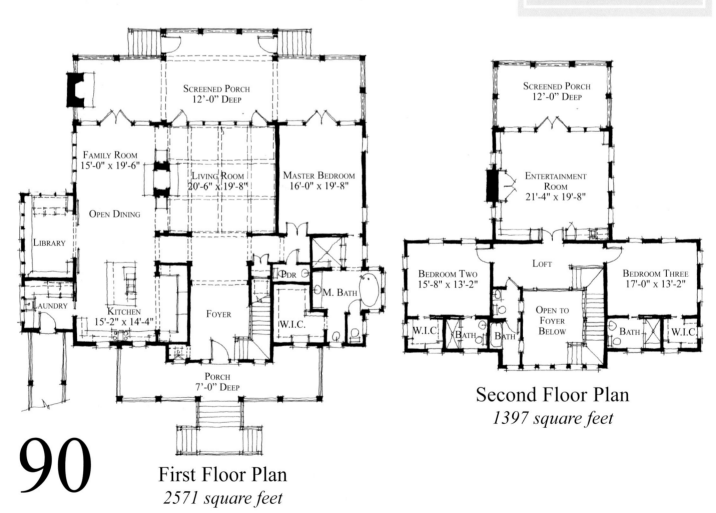

90

First Floor Plan
2571 square feet

Second Floor Plan
1397 square feet

ARA
ALLISON RAMSEY
Architects *Inc.* creating sustainable timeless design

THE BRISTOL

WWW.ALLISONRAMSEYARCHITECTS.COM/
THEBRISOL.PDF

Identification #
C0591
Heated square feet

1682

Overall Dimensions
26'-0" x 57'-0"

Height to Ridge
26'-7"

3 Bed/ 2 1/2 Bath

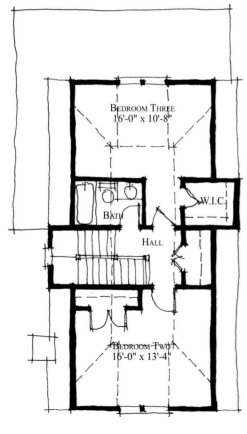

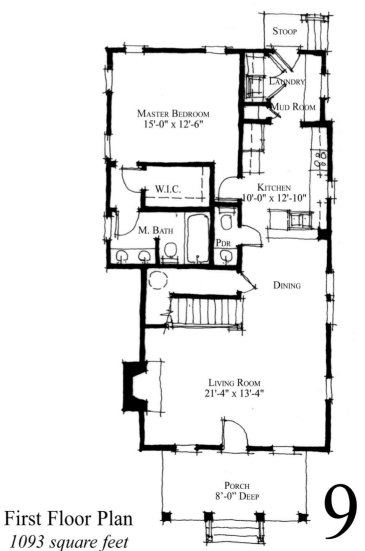

Second Floor Plan
589 square feet

First Floor Plan
1093 square feet

91

ALLISON RAMSEY
Architects Inc.   creating sustainable timeless design

MOCKBEE COTTAGE

WWW.ALLISONRAMSEYARCHITECTS.COM/
MOCKBEECOTTAGE.PDF

Identification #
C0592
Heated square feet
1659
Overall Dimensions
36'-10" x 64'-0"
Height to Ridge
21'-2"

3 Bed/ 3 1/2 Bath

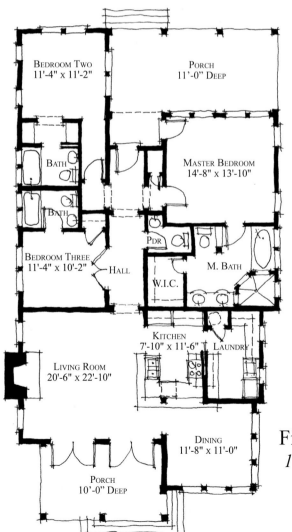

BEDROOM TWO
11'-4" x 11'-2"

PORCH
11'-0" DEEP

BATH

BATH

MASTER BEDROOM
14'-8" x 13'-10"

BEDROOM THREE
11'-4" x 10'-2"

HALL

PDR

M. BATH

W.I.C.

KITCHEN
7'-10" x 11'-6"

LAUNDRY

LIVING ROOM
20'-6" x 22'-10"

DINING
11'-8" x 11'-0"

First Floor Plan
1659 square feet

PORCH
10'-0" DEEP

92

ALLISON RAMSEY
Architects Inc. creating sustainable timeless design

HARPERS RIDGE

*WWW.ALLISONRAMSEYARCHITECTS.COM/
HARPERSRIDGE.PDF*

Identification #
C0593
Heated square feet

2534

Overall Dimensions
46'-0" x 62'-0"

Height to Ridge
27'-2"

4 Bed/ 3 Bath

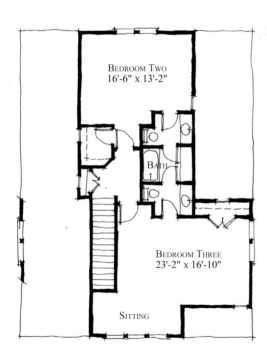

Second Floor Plan
791 square feet

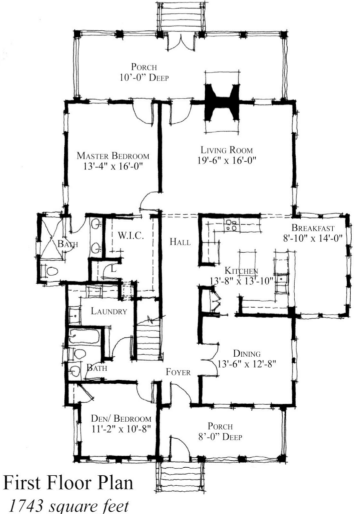

First Floor Plan
1743 square feet

93

ALLISON RAMSEY

Architects Inc. creating sustainable timeless design

NEW FARMHOUSE

WWW.ALLISONRAMSEYARCHITECTS.COM/
NEWFARMHOUSE.PDF

Identification #
C0594
Heated square feet

2846

Overall Dimensions
54'-0" x 105'-2"

Height to Ridge
32'-3"

3 Bed/ 2 1/2 Bath

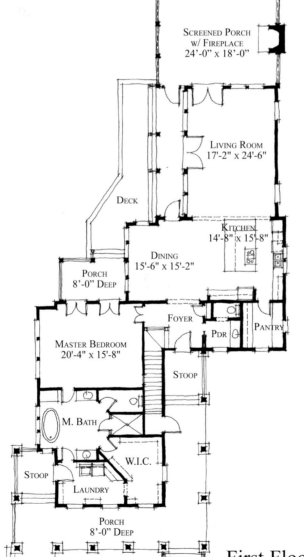

SCREENED PORCH
W/ FIREPLACE
24'-0" x 18'-0"

LIVING ROOM
17'-2" x 24'-6"

DECK

KITCHEN
14'-8" x 15'-8"

DINING
15'-6" x 15'-2"

PORCH
8'-0" DEEP

FOYER

PANTRY

PDR

MASTER BEDROOM
20'-4" x 15'-8"

STOOP

M. BATH

STOOP

W.I.C.

LAUNDRY

PORCH
8'-0" DEEP

Breezeway to Garage
or Guest House

First Floor Plan
2075 square feet

DECK
8' DEEP

BEDROOM THREE
21'-0" x 12'-2"

W.I.C.

SHARED
BATH

W.I.C. HALL

BEDROOM TWO
21'-0" x 12'-3"

Second Floor Plan
771 square feet

94

NEWPORT
BEACH

WWW.ALLISONRAMSEYARCHITECTS.COM/
NEWPORTBEACH.PDF

Identification #
C0595
Heated square feet

2545

Overall Dimensions
36'-0" x 57'-0"

Height to Ridge
31'-9"

4 Bed/ 4 1/2 Bath

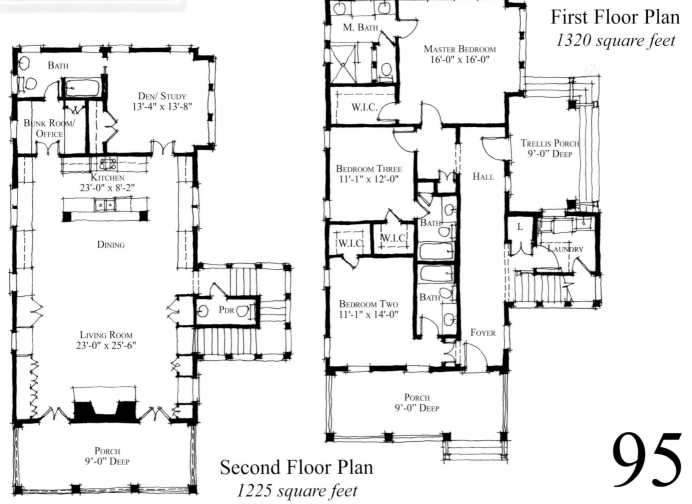

BATH

DEN/ STUDY
13'-4" x 13'-8"

BUNK ROOM/ OFFICE

KITCHEN
23'-0" x 8'-2"

DINING

PDR

LIVING ROOM
23'-0" x 25'-6"

PORCH
9'-0" DEEP

Second Floor Plan
1225 square feet

M. BATH

MASTER BEDROOM
16'-0" x 16'-0"

First Floor Plan
1320 square feet

W.I.C.

BEDROOM THREE
11'-1" x 12'-0"

HALL

TRELLIS PORCH
9'-0" DEEP

BATH

W.I.C.

W.I.C.

L

LAUNDRY

BEDROOM TWO
11'-1" x 14'-0"

BATH

FOYER

PORCH
9'-0" DEEP

95

NEWPOINT GUESTHOUSE

WWW.ALLISONRAMSEYARCHITECTS.COM/
NEWPOINTGUESTHOUSE.PDF

Identification #

C0596

Heated square feet

283

Overall Dimensions

16'-0" x 21'-8"

Height to Ridge

14'-4"

0 Bed/ 1 Bath

BATH

W.I.C.

LIVING/ KITCHEN
15'-4" x 11'-8"

PORCH/ STOOP
4'-0" DEEP

First Floor Plan
283 square feet

96

SAPELO SOUND

WWW.ALLISONRAMSEYARCHITECTS.COM/
SAPELOSOUND.PDF

Identification #
C0597
Heated square feet

3209

Overall Dimensions
90'-0" x 78'-6"

Height to Ridge
23'-8"

3 Bed/ 3 1/2 Bath

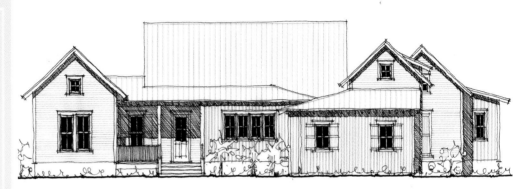

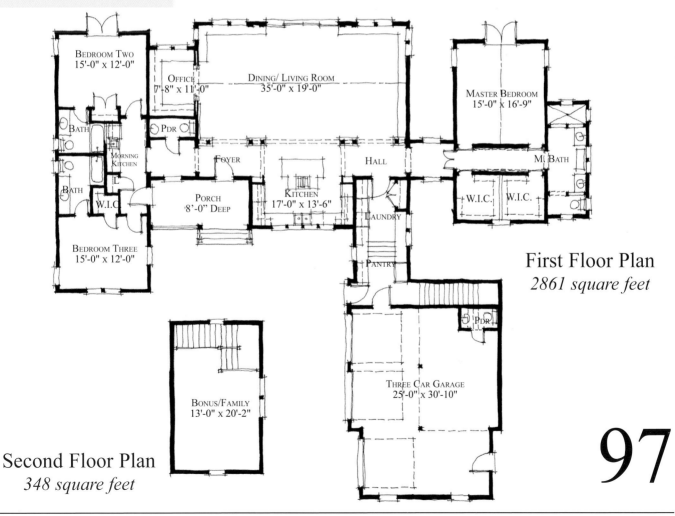

First Floor Plan
2861 square feet

Second Floor Plan
348 square feet

97

ALLISON RAMSEY
Architects *Inc.* creating sustainable timeless design

THE VERDIER

WWW.ALLISONRAMSEYARCHITECTS.COM/
THEVERDIER.PDF

Identification #
C0012
Heated square feet

1726

Overall Dimensions
28'-0" x 61'-0"

Height to Ridge
24'-4"

3 Bed/ 2 1/2 Bath

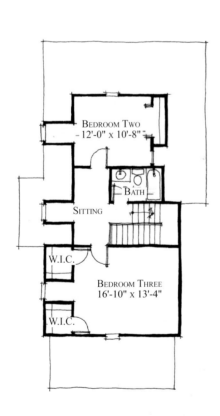

Second Floor Plan
624 square feet

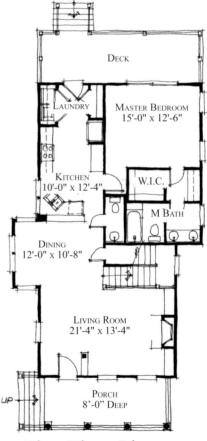

First Floor Plan
1102 square feet

ALLISON RAMSEY
Architects Inc. creating sustainable timeless design

THE VERDIER is a more formal take on a classic southern cottage. It has an upright yet simple form combining classical elements with a symetrical facade. A paneled parapet adorns the porch roof and is the architectural element that completes the Verdier's personality. The floor plan is open and bright, the Master Bedroom is downstairs, and the two bedrooms upstairs are generous . The floor plan is exceptionally functional and easy to live in. The look is traditional and lovable. The Verdier is great for narrow lots and corner lots in any neighborhood. It has been proven many times, in many great neighborhoods.

RENDERING FROM SOUTHERN LIVING PUBLICATIONS

THE VERDIER WAS THE COTTAGE LIVING "PLAN OF THE MONTH" IN APRIL 2008.

99

ALLISON RAMSEY
Architects Inc. creating sustainable timeless design

NORTH STREET
WWW.ALLISONRAMSEYARCHITECTS.COM/
NORTHSTREET.PDF

Identification #
C0600
Heated square feet

2960

Overall Dimensions
29'-0" x 78'-0"

Height to Ridge
30'-9"

4 Bed/ 4 Bath

First Floor Plan
1489 square feet

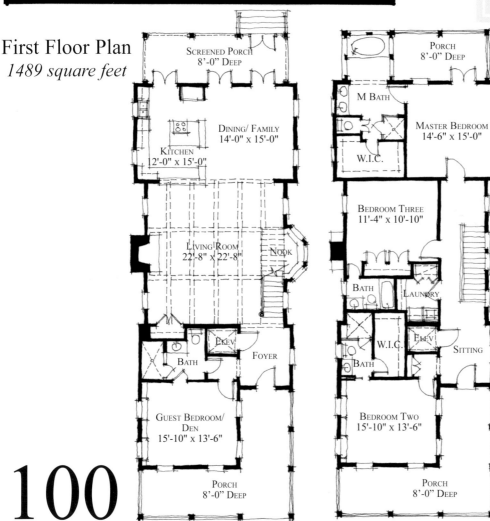

SCREENED PORCH
8'-0" DEEP

DINING/ FAMILY
14'-0" x 15'-0"

KITCHEN
12'-0" x 15'-0"

LIVING ROOM
22'-8" x 22'-8"

NOOK

ELEV

BATH

FOYER

GUEST BEDROOM/
DEN
15'-10" x 13'-6"

PORCH
8'-0" DEEP

PORCH
8'-0" DEEP

M BATH

MASTER BEDROOM
14'-6" x 15'-0"

W.I.C.

BEDROOM THREE
11'-4" x 10'-10"

BATH

LAUNDRY

W.I.C.

ELEV

SITTING

BATH

BEDROOM TWO
15'-10" x 13'-6"

PORCH
8'-0" DEEP

Second Floor Plan
1471 square feet

100

ARA
ALLISON RAMSEY
Architects Inc. creating sustainable timeless design

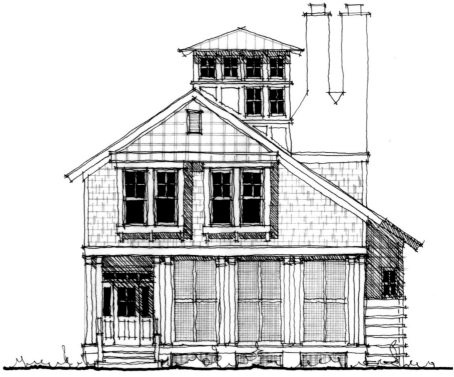

FIDDLER'S TOWER II

WWW.ALLISONRAMSEYARCHITECTS.COM/FID-DLERSTOWERII.PDF

Identification #
C0601
Heated square feet

2673

Overall Dimensions
35'-0" x 61'-4"

Height to Ridge
34'-1"

4 Bed/ 4 1/2 Bath

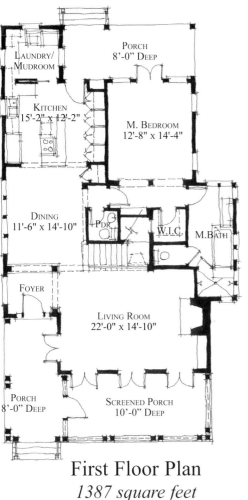

LAUNDRY/ MUDROOM

PORCH 8'-0" DEEP

KITCHEN 15'-2" x 12'-2"

M. BEDROOM 12'-8" x 14'-4"

DINING 11'-6" x 14'-10"

PDR.

W.I.C.

M.BATH

FOYER

LIVING ROOM 22'-0" x 14'-10"

PORCH 8'-0" DEEP

SCREENED PORCH 10'-0" DEEP

First Floor Plan
1387 square feet

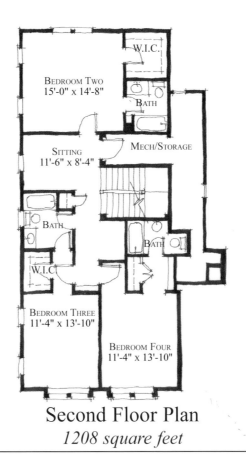

W.I.C.

BEDROOM TWO 15'-0" x 14'-8"

BATH

SITTING 11'-6" x 8'-4"

MECH/STORAGE

BATH

BATH

W.I.C

BEDROOM THREE 11'-4" x 13'-10"

BEDROOM FOUR 11'-4" x 13'-10"

Second Floor Plan
1208 square feet

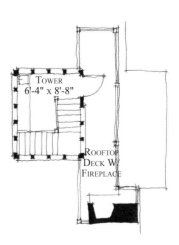

TOWER 6'-4" x 8'-8"

ROOFTOP DECK W/ FIREPLACE

Tower Plan
78 square feet

101

ALLISON RAMSEY
Architects Inc. creating sustainable timeless design

THE
GEORGETOWN

WWW.ALLISONRAMSEYARCHITECTS.COM/
THEGEORGETOWN.PDF

Identification #
C0602
Heated square feet

2566

Overall Dimensions
47'-4" x 56'-0"

Height to Ridge
27'-9"

3 Bed/ 3 1/2 Bath

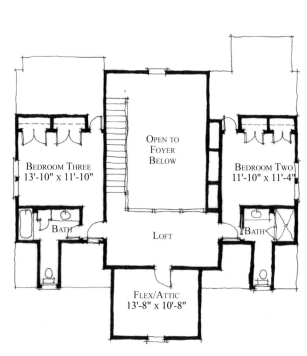

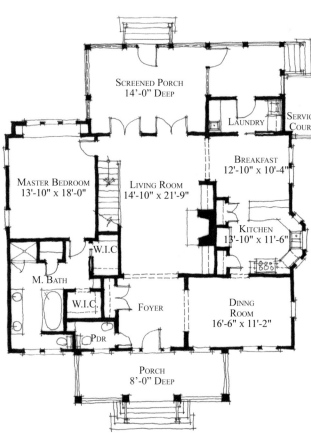

102

Second Floor Plan
919 square feet

First Floor Plan
1647 square feet

ALLISON RAMSEY
Architects *Inc.* creating sustainable timeless design

ALTAMAHA
RIVER COTTAGE

WWW.ALLISONRAMSEYARCHITECTS.COM/
ALTAMAHARIVERCOTTAGE.PDF

Identification #
C0603
Heated square feet

1492

Overall Dimensions
23'-10" x 60'-0"

Height to Ridge
24'-0"

3 Bed/ 2 1/2 Bath

Bedroom Two
13'-8" x 12'-4"

Loft

Bath

Open to Foyer Below

Laundry

Bedroom Three
13'-8" x 13'-4"

Second Floor Plan
667 square feet

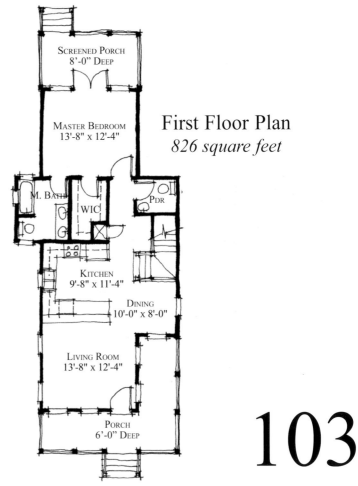

Screened Porch
8'-0" Deep

Master Bedroom
13'-8" x 12'-4"

First Floor Plan
826 square feet

M. Bath

WIC

Pdr

Kitchen
9'-8" x 11'-4"

Dining
10'-0" x 8'-0"

Living Room
13'-8" x 12'-4"

Porch
6'-0" Deep

103

ARA
ALLISON RAMSEY
Architects Inc. creating sustainable timeless design

HUNT CLUB
WWW.ALLISONRAMSEYARCHITECTS.COM/
HUNTCLUB.PDF

Identification #
C0604
Heated square feet
973
Overall Dimensions
55'-0" x 40'-10"
Height to Ridge
20'-3"

1 Bed/ 1 Bath

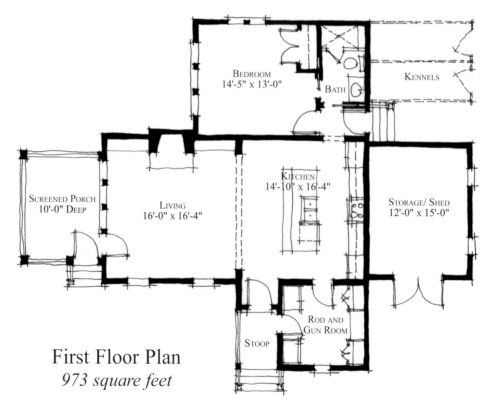

BEDROOM
14'-5" x 13'-0"

BATH

KENNELS

SCREENED PORCH
10'-0" DEEP

LIVING
16'-0" x 16'-4"

KITCHEN
14'-10" x 16'-4"

STORAGE/ SHED
12'-0" x 15'-0"

STOOP

ROD AND
GUN ROOM

First Floor Plan
973 square feet

104

ARA
ALLISON RAMSEY
Architects *Inc.* creating sustainable timeless design

THE LAUREL HILL
WWW.ALLISONRAMSEYARCHITECTS.COM/
THELAURELHILL.PDF

Identification #
C0605
Heated square feet
2679

Overall Dimensions
46'-0" x 60'-6"

Height to Ridge
24'-8"

4 Bed/ 3 Bath

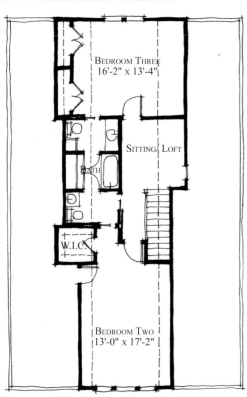

Second Floor Plan
824 square feet

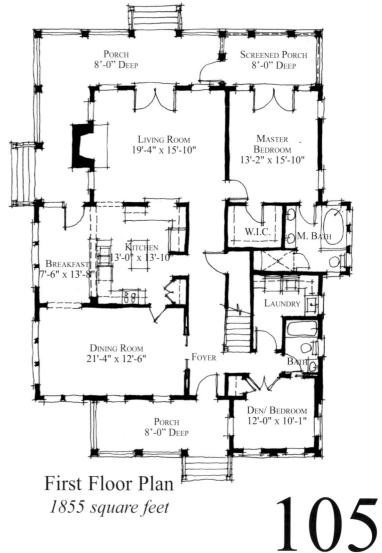

First Floor Plan
1855 square feet

105

BRADDOCK COVE COTTAGE

WWW.ALLISONRAMSEYARCHITECTS.COM/
BRADDOCKCOVECOTTAGE.PDF

Identification #
C0606
Heated square feet

2699

Overall Dimensions
67'-0" x 56'-4"

Height to Ridge
28'-0"

3 Bed/3 1/2 Bath

Second Floor Plan
650 square feet

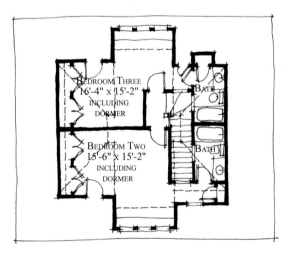

BEDROOM THREE 16'-4" x 15'-2" INCLUDING DORMER

BATH

BEDROOM TWO 15'-6" x 15'-2" INCLUDING DORMER

BATH

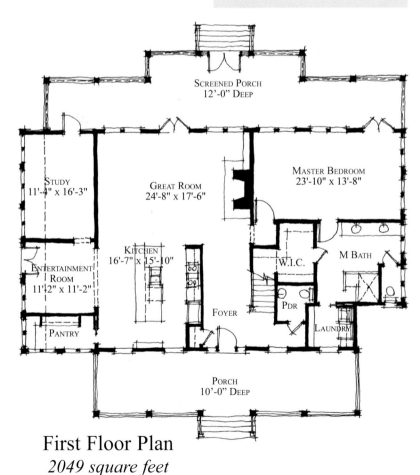

SCREENED PORCH 12'-0" DEEP

STUDY 11'-4" x 16'-3"

GREAT ROOM 24'-8" x 17'-6"

MASTER BEDROOM 23'-10" x 13'-8"

ENTERTAINMENT ROOM 11'2" x 11'-2"

KITCHEN 16'-7" x 15'-10"

W.I.C.

M BATH

PANTRY

FOYER

PDR

LAUNDRY

PORCH 10'-0" DEEP

First Floor Plan
2049 square feet

106

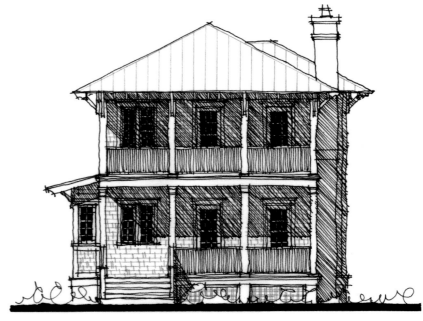

ARA
ALLISON RAMSEY
Architects Inc. creating sustainable timeless design

THE GRAYTON BEACH

WWW.ALLISONRAMSEYARCHITECTS.COM/
THEGRAYTONBEACH.PDF

Identification #
C0607
Heated square feet

2081

Overall Dimensions
32'-6" x 81'-4"

Height to Ridge
29'-2"

4 Bed/ 3 1/2 Bath

Second Floor Plan
791 square feet

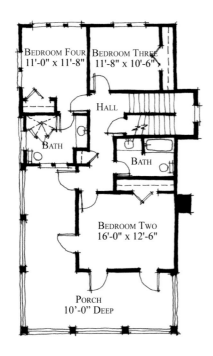

First Floor Plan
1290 square feet

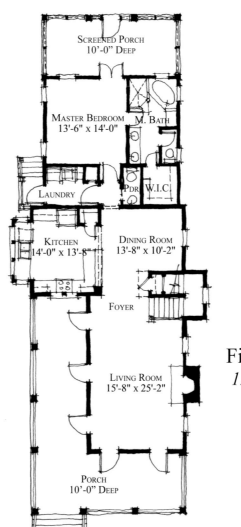

107

ALLISON RAMSEY
Architects *Inc.* creating sustainable timeless design

TERREBONNE

*WWW.ALLISONRAMSEYARCHITECTS.COM/
TERREBONNE.PDF*

Identification #
C0608
Heated square feet

2737

Overall Dimensions
51'-0" x 54'-0"

Height to Ridge
33'-7"

3 Bed/ 3 1/2 Bath

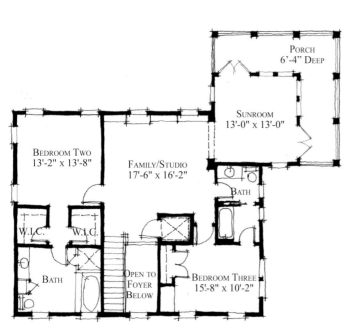

Second Floor Plan
1221 square feet

108

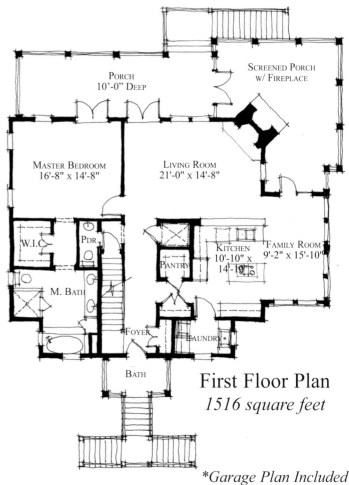

First Floor Plan
1516 square feet

Garage Plan Included

THE PEPPER
BEACH

WWW.ALLISONRAMSEYARCHITECTS.COM/
THEPEPPERBEACH.PDF

Identification #
C0609
Heated square feet

2296

Overall Dimensions
59'-0" x 49'-8"

Height to Ridge
29'-8"

3 Bed/ 3 1/2 Bath

First Floor Plan
1190 square feet

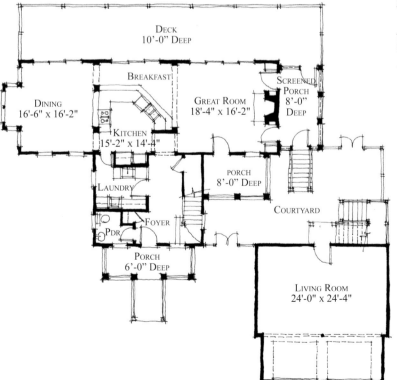

DECK
10'-0" DEEP

BREAKFAST

DINING
16'-6" x 16'-2"

GREAT ROOM
18'-4" x 16'-2"

SCREENED
PORCH
8'-0"
DEEP

KITCHEN
15'-2" x 14'-4"

LAUNDRY

PORCH
8'-0" DEEP

FOYER

PDR

COURTYARD

PORCH
6'-0" DEEP

LIVING ROOM
24'-0" x 24'-4"

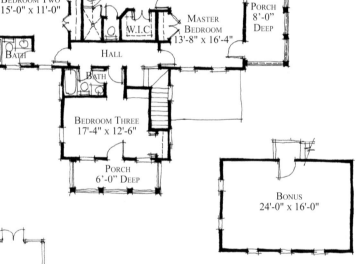

BEDROOM TWO
15'-0" x 11'-0"

M. BATH

SCREENED
PORCH
8'-0"
DEEP

W.I.C

MASTER
BEDROOM
13'-8" x 16'-4"

BATH

HALL

BATH

BEDROOM THREE
17'-4" x 12'-6"

PORCH
6'-0" DEEP

BONUS
24'-0" x 16'-0"

Second Floor Plan
1106 square feet

109

ALLISON RAMSEY
Architects Inc. creating sustainable timeless design

HORSESHOE MANOR

WWW.ALLISONRAMSEYARCHITECTS.COM/
HORSESHOEMANOR.PDF

Identification #

C0610
Heated square feet

4525
Overall Dimensions

51'-4" x 61'-4"

Height to Ridge

37'-8"

4 Bed/ 4 Bath

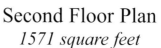
Second Floor Plan
1571 square feet

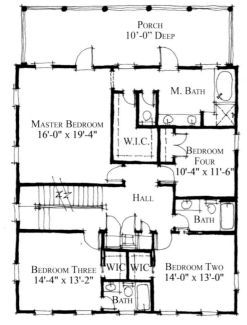

PORCH 10'-0" DEEP

M. BATH

MASTER BEDROOM 16'-0" x 19'-4"

W.I.C.

BEDROOM FOUR 10'-4" x 11'-6"

HALL

BATH

BEDROOM THREE 14'-4" x 13'-2"

WIC WIC

BATH

BEDROOM TWO 14'-0" x 13'-0"

Loft Plan
1114 square feet

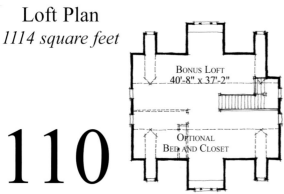

BONUS LOFT 40'-8" x 37'-2"

OPTIONAL BED AND CLOSET

110

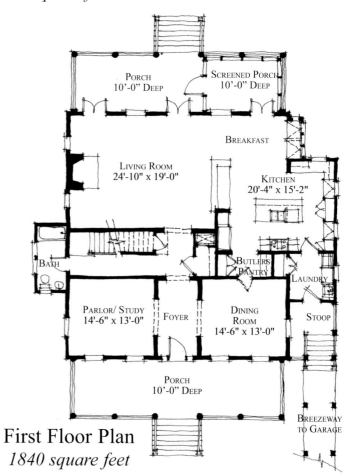

PORCH 10'-0" DEEP

SCREENED PORCH 10'-0" DEEP

BREAKFAST

LIVING ROOM 24'-10" x 19'-0"

KITCHEN 20'-4" x 15'-2"

BATH

BUTLERS PANTRY

LAUNDRY

PARLOR/ STUDY 14'-6" x 13'-0"

FOYER

DINING ROOM 14'-6" x 13'-0"

STOOP

PORCH 10'-0" DEEP

BREEZEWAY TO GARAGE

First Floor Plan
1840 square feet

ALLISON RAMSEY
Architects Inc.   creating sustainable timeless design

NEVIN'S NEST

WWW.ALLISONRAMSEYARCHITECTS.COM/
NEVINSNEST.PDF

Identification #
C0611
Heated square feet

1899 w/ loft

Overall Dimensions
26'-10" x 61'-0"

Height to Ridge
26'-10"

2 Bed/ 2 Bath

First Floor Plan
1122 square feet

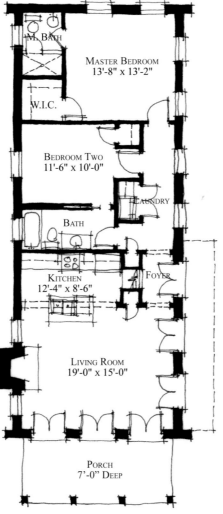

M. BATH

MASTER BEDROOM
13'-8" x 13'-2"

W.I.C.

BEDROOM TWO
11'-6" x 10'-0"

LAUNDRY

BATH

KITCHEN
12'-4" x 8'-6"

FOYER

LIVING ROOM
19'-0" x 15'-0"

PORCH
7'-0" DEEP

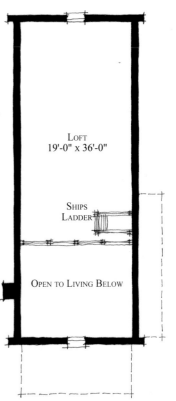

LOFT
19'-0" x 36'-0"

SHIPS
LADDER

OPEN TO LIVING BELOW

Loft Floor Plan
777 square feet

111

ALLISON RAMSEY
Architects Inc. creating sustainable timeless design

ARCHING OAKS

*WWW.ALLISONRAMSEYARCHITECTS.COM/
ARCHINGOAKS.PDF*

Identification #

C0612
Heated square feet

1287

Overall Dimensions
19'-6" x 51'-8"

Height to Ridge
24'-1"

3 Bed/ 2 Bath

First Floor Plan
677 square feet

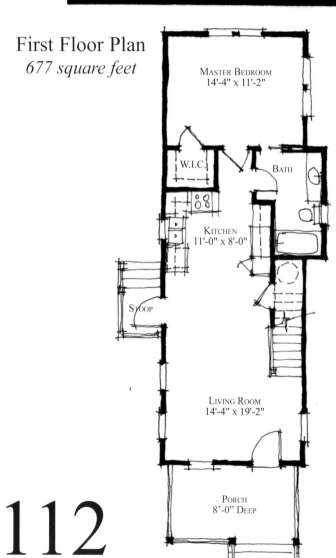

MASTER BEDROOM
14'-4" x 11'-2"

W.I.C.

BATH

KITCHEN
11'-0" x 8'-0"

STOOP

LIVING ROOM
14'-4" x 19'-2"

PORCH
8'-0" Deep

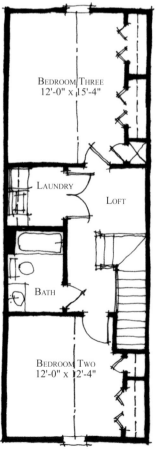

BEDROOM THREE
12'-0" x 15'-4"

LAUNDRY

LOFT

BATH

BEDROOM TWO
12'-0" x 12'-4"

Second Floor Plan
610 square feet

112

Noah's Cottage

WWW.ALLISONRAMSEYARCHITECTS.COM/
NOAHSCOTTAGE.PDF

Identification #

C0613

Heated square feet

1806 without loft

Overall Dimensions
46'-0" x 54'-2"

Height to Ridge
21'-10"

3 Bed/ 2 Bath

*Use of loft as habitable space
should be verified w/ local codes
prior to purchase*

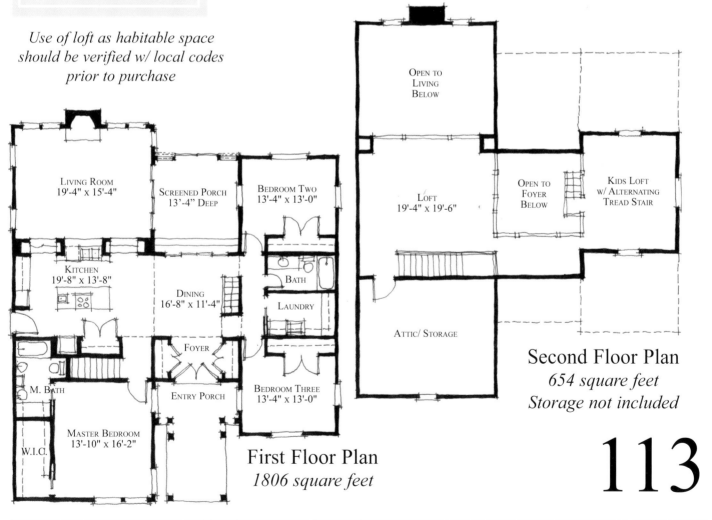

First Floor Plan
1806 square feet

Second Floor Plan
*654 square feet
Storage not included*

113

ALLISON RAMSEY
Architects *Inc.* creating sustainable timeless design

ALBEMARLE
CABIN

WWW.ALLISONRAMSEYARCHITECTS.COM/
ALBEMARLECABIN.PDF

Identification #
C0614
Heated square feet

824

Overall Dimensions
16'-0" x 43'-8"

Height to Ridge
24'-4"

2 Bed/ 2 Bath

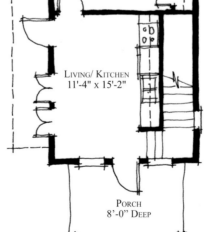

BEDROOM
15'-0" x 11'-0"

BATH

LIVING/ KITCHEN
11'-4" x 15'-2"

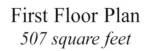

PORCH
8'-0" DEEP

First Floor Plan
507 square feet

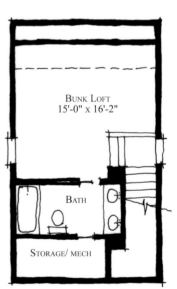

BUNK LOFT
15'-0" x 16'-2"

BATH

STORAGE/ MECH

Second Floor Plan
317 square feet

114

ALLISON RAMSEY
Architects Inc. creating sustainable timeless design

MOUNT HOLLY

WWW.ALLISONRAMSEYARCHITECTS.COM/
MOUNTHOLLY.PDF

Identification #
C0615
Heated square feet
2627

Overall Dimensions
32'-0" x 63'-2"

Height to Ridge
29'-0"

4 Bed/ 4 1/2 Bath

First Floor Plan
1457 square feet

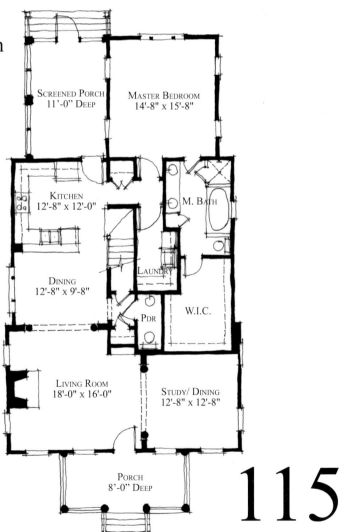

SCREENED PORCH 11'-0" DEEP

MASTER BEDROOM 14'-8" x 15'-8"

KITCHEN 12'-8" x 12'-0"

M. BATH

DINING 12'-8" x 9'-8"

LAUNDRY

PDR

W.I.C.

LIVING ROOM 18'-0" x 16'-0"

STUDY/ DINING 12'-8" x 12'-8"

PORCH 8'-0" DEEP

Second Floor Plan
1170 square feet

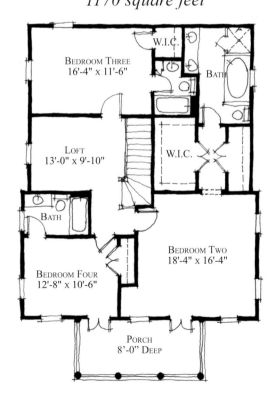

BEDROOM THREE 16'-4" x 11'-6"

W.I.C.

BATH

LOFT 13'-0" x 9'-10"

W.I.C.

BATH

BEDROOM TWO 18'-4" x 16'-4"

BEDROOM FOUR 12'-8" x 10'-6"

PORCH 8'-0" DEEP

115

ALLISON RAMSEY
Architects Inc. creating sustainable timeless design

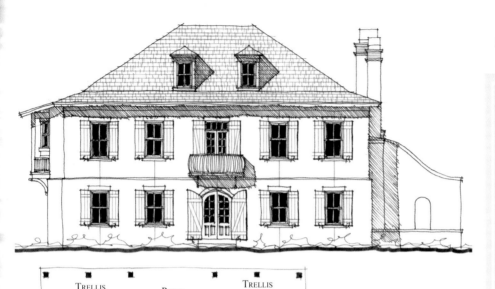

TUSCARORA

WWW.ALLISONRAMSEYARCHITECTS.COM/
TUSCARORA.PDF

Identification #
C0616
Heated square feet
3863
Overall Dimensions
67'-0" x 52'-6"
Height to Ridge
35'-4"

4 Bed/ 4 Bath

TRELLIS PATIO

PATIO

TRELLIS PATIO

BEDROOM 3
15'-10" x 14'-0"

SCREEN PORCH
11'-0" DEEP

BATH

BEDROOM 4
15'-0" x 10'-8"

HALL

BATH

MECH/ STORAGE

TWO CAR GARAGE

ELEV

STUDY
21'-0" x 16'-4"

PATIO

FOYER

First Floor Plan
1630 square feet

Second Floor Plan
2233 square feet

TRELLIS BELOW

TRELLIS BELOW

BREAKFAST
21'-2" x 8'-10"

PORCH
9'-0" DEEP

KITCHEN
14'-8" x 14'-10"

ENTRY

GREAT ROOM
27'-10" x 19'-10"

BALCONY

BATH

BEDROOM TWO
15'-2" x 10'-10"

WIC

WIC

M. BEDROOM
18'-0" x 15'-8"

SITTING
9'-7" x 13'-10

M.BATH

BALCONY

TUSCARORA

With spectacular views out of the rear of this home, this "upside down" plan is a unique twist on retirement living. Beautiful vaulted ceilings in the great room, kitchen, and breakfast rooms, along with a generously proportioned open floor plan make this house ideal for entertaining. The main living floor includes a guest bedroom and master "suite". Downstairs features two additional bedrooms along with an office/study with its own fireplace. The garage is built-in to this house, making it extremely convenient. The home's elevator allows the plan to be easily modified to allow accessibility for those with disabilities or with mobility concerns. Wide porches upstairs and down, which act as outdoor "rooms", complete this very livable house plan.

117

Important Copyright Notice from Allison Ramsey Architects

The designs and plans in this book were drawn and created solely by architects employed by Allison Ramsey Architects of Beaufort, South Carolina. The designs are the express property of the firm. This book as well as individual plans and designs contained in this book are copyrighted with the United States Copyright Office pursuant to Title 17 U.S.C. ß 101 et, seg. As such, the plans, renderings, and designs are the property of Allison Ramsey Architects.

House Plans are Copyrighted
Like authors, photographers, and musicians, architects are protected by copyright laws. Federal laws were established to safeguard the intellectual property of architects. Copyright laws prohibit using an architect's designs or drawings without written permission of the architect.

If You Want to Build, Buy the Plan
The variety of designs presented in this book should help you find a house in keeping with your property, budget, and lifestyle. If you plan to build one of the designs featured here, you must purchase a set of plans from Allison Ramsey Architects.

Don't Copy These Plans
It is against the law to copy designs or drawings found in plan books, magazines, or on the Internet. Many people believe it's acceptable to copy or adapt a design from a publication or the web and build a house. Copying any existing built home or house plan that is copyrighted is not allowed--it's illegal.

Modifying a Design
Once you have purchased a plan from Allison Ramsey Architects, it can be modified by us or by another designer, architect, engineer, or builder. We encourage you to customize your plan. If you choose to modify our design, we hope you ask us to adapt the plan to fit your personal needs and preferences. If you do make changes, please know that any modification by others to a plan is made at your own risk and should be reviewed by a professional residential designer or engineer before starting construction. In addition, these modified plans are considered "derivative works" of the original design, and Allison Ramsey Architects retains copyright protection on the original design and any "derivative work."

One -Time Rights
All house plans include a copyright release and a license to use the documents to build one home. The purchase of a set of these construction documents grants permission to use the plans to build a single structure. Don't use our plans to build more than one house. This is an exclusive license, which may not be resold or reproduced without permission of Allison Ramsey Architects.

Conditions of Using a Plan
As the homeowner or contractor who purchases an Allison Ramsey plan, you may lend the plan to third parties (builders, subcontactors, inspectors, review boards, or government agencies) to assist with approvals, budgets, and construction of the residence.

Copyright Infringement and Penalties
Any party, including the purchaser, homeowner, builder, drafter, or contractor, may be responsible if a copyright is violated. Refuse to be involved with any questionable copying of plans, borrowing of designs, or using derivative works. Penalties for copyright infringement can be severe, including actual damages, statutory damages, and reimbursement of reasonable legal fees.

Please Respect Our Copyright